D1632280

This edition published by Parragon Books Ltd in 2015

Parragon Books Ltd
Chartist House
15–17 Trim Street
Bath BA1 1HA, UK
www.parragon.com

Copyright © Parragon Books Ltd 2015

Manuscript © Michael Powell 2012
Contents designed by Peter Wilkinson

All rights reserved. No part of this publication may be
reproduced, stored in a retrieval system or transmitted,
in any form or by any means, electronic, mechanical,
photocopying, recording or otherwise, without the
prior permission of the copyright holder.

ISBN: 978-1-4723-6419-7

Printed in China

OLD WIVES' TALES

SUPERSTITION AND MYTH DEMYSTIFIED!

Bath • New York • Cologne • Melbourne • Delhi
Hong Kong • Shenzhen • Singapore • Amsterdam

 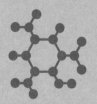

Introduction

/ Old wives' tales have their roots in the rich oral tradition of storytelling. Today they are for the most part ridiculed as superstition and unscientific and it is tempting to believe that our modern understanding of physics, chemistry and biology can supply all the answers.

The *Oxford English Dictionary* defines an old wives' tale as "a foolish story, such as is told by garrulous old women". At times, they have even been considered sinful. In the first century AD, the Apostle Paul advised Timothy to "refuse profane and old wives' fables, and exercise thyself (rather) unto godliness" (I Timothy 4:7).

This information was handed down the generations by illiterate women, telling stories to each other or to children, which is why so many of them are concerned with the spheres of activity to which they were most usually confined, such as pregnancy and childbirth, health and the household.

Writing in the *Guardian* recently, Germaine Greer lamented: "Most of women's poetry and storytelling has been swallowed up in the maw of time. Because the authors of old wives' tales were not literate . . . because the people who told them were women and the people who heard them were children, they were phenomena of no account. From the earliest times, such narratives have been treated with contempt."

But sometimes the oldest advice is resolutely the best, as Celeborn advises Boromir in *Lord of the Rings*: "Do not despise the lore that has come down from distant years; for oft it may chance that old wives keep in memory word of things that once were needful for the wise to know." A fair number of these so-called superstitions are supported by modern science and deserve re-evaluation.

Many are plain wrong *(putting butter on a burn eases the pain)*; some are right for the wrong reasons *(sugar makes children hyperactive)* or wrong for the right reasons *(eating carrots helps you see in the dark)*; some were true in their time but are no longer relevant *(whistling on stage brings bad luck)*; others have expedient origins but are coincidentally true *(eating your crusts is good for you)*; a few have been rediscovered by modern research *(sage is good for the memory)* and most intriguingly of all, a handful continue to enjoy strong anecdotal support even though the science remains equivocal: *(cure leg cramps by sleeping with a bar of soap)*.

Unfortunately, sometimes the oldest advice is simply the oldest and there is still confusion among the general public about which old wives' tales are true (or partially true) and which invite our scorn. Which is where this book comes in. Using the latest scientific research we examine the origins and reliability of more than fifty common old wives' tales to explore how and why they arose and how they influence us today.

5

Contents

"Eating carrots helps you see in the dark"

/Carrots are a rich source of beta-carotene, one of more than 600 organic pigments called carotenoids known to exist in nature. About fifty of these can be used in the body to make Vitamin A, which is essential for good vision and especially night vision. One of the first signs that a person is deficient in Vitamin A is a reduction in night vision. However, a healthy person who is already receiving sufficient levels of beta-carotene or other precursors of Vitamin A in their diet (such as retinol, the most common animal-based source, found in meat, fish oils, eggs and dairy products) will not improve their night vision by eating more carrots.

The area within the eye that detects light and colour is called the retina, and has two types of detection cells – rods and cones. Beta-carotene is important for night vision because the retina uses it to produce a form of Vitamin A called Retinal, which is combined with a protein called opsin to make the purple photosensitive pigment Rhodopsin. This is used in the rod cells which only work in low light.

Vitamin A deficiency also leads to an increased incidence of cataracts, glaucoma and macular degeneration. So it makes sense to include plenty of carrots in your daily diet. Massive overconsumption of carrots causes a temporary non-fatal condition called carotenosis, which turns the skin orange, but you'd have to drink several pints of carrot juice every day to have this effect. In 1974, Basil Brown, a 48-year-old scientific adviser from Croydon, died after drinking a gallon of carrot juice every day for ten days, but it was probably the extreme doses of the retinol form of Vitamin A supplement he also took which caused his fatal cirrhosis of the liver.

During the Second World War carrots played a prominent role on the home front. They were plentiful and frequently used as a substitute for scarcer foodstuffs in recipes. Dr Carrot was a star player in the Ministry of Agriculture's Dig for Victory poster campaign to encourage everyone to grow their own food. Carrots also became synonymous with night vision because the link was exaggerated by allied propaganda. The allies had recently invented RADAR and used it to shoot down many more German planes during night sorties, so they put out the story that air crews were eating lots of carrots to disguise the real reason for their success. Carrots are one of the richest natural sources of beta-carotene but there are many others including broccoli, kale, spinach, sweet potatoes, pumpkins, winter squash, apricots, cantaloupes, papayas, mangoes, nectarines and peaches. If any one of these beta-carotene-rich foods had been chosen instead to fool the enemy, they would have the same prominence in the public consciousness today as carrots do for improving night vision.

>Verdict

Eating carrots will only improve your night vision if you are already deficient in Vitamin A.

"Gain a child, lose a tooth"

/This is one of the most well-known old wives' tales relating to women's health, but research has shown a link between the number of pregnancies and diminished dental health.

In 2005, the New York University College of Dentistry examined 2,635 women aged 18 to 64 who had carried at least one pregnancy to term and found that many reported dental problems. The study found an increased risk of gingivitis and periodontal disease. However, debate continues about the various causes of this increased risk. Here are some likely reasons:

1. Morning sickness erodes the teeth. Persistent vomiting from *Hyperemesis gravidarum* (morning sickness) causes acid erosion of the teeth from the strong stomach acids. Morning sickness affects up to 80 per cent of all pregnant women to some degree. Usually it subsides by the 16th week of pregnancy, but 20 per cent of women continue to have symptoms throughout pregnancy.

2. Pregnant women and mothers may also be reluctant or too busy to visit the dentist so any dental problems are detected late.

A study at the Centers for Disease Control and Prevention (CDC) found that roughly a quarter of pregnant women surveyed reported dental problems but just half of them sought treatment.

3. Pregnancy draws heavily on the mother's resources of vitamins and minerals and depletes her calcium, weakening the teeth. It is true that when body stores of calcium are low, it must take calcium from the teeth and bones, but research suggests that the extra calcium required for the foetus is provided not by drawing on skeletal calcium of the mother but by increasing the intestinal absorption of calcium in her diet, so if she is eating a balanced diet she shouldn't suffer bone and teeth damage.

4. Many pregnant women experience bleeding gums while brushing or flossing. This is because the hormone progesterone softens the gums and the increased blood supply makes them more likely to react to the bacteria in plaque.

5. Skeletal calcium depletion can be caused by breastfeeding. The typical daily loss of calcium in breast milk has been estimated to range from 280–400mg, although daily losses as great as 1,000mg have been reported. In *Calcium and Bone Metabolism in Pregnancy and Lactation,* Christopher S. Kovacs says: "A temporary demineralization of the skeleton seems to be the main mechanism by which lactating women meet these calcium requirements."

6. Mothers are less healthy than childless women. Dr Jerica Berge of the University of Minnesota analysed the dietary and exercise habits of young parents with children under five. The mothers had higher body mass indices than women without children and took less exercise. Their diets also suffered. Add to this sleep deprivation and mums have a potent cocktail of health stressors.

>Verdict

Studies have found a clear link between pregnancy and motherhood and dental problems but the multiple causes are moot.

" Feed a cold, starve a fever "

/The traditional lore is to feed a cold and starve a fever and an early example of this advice appears in a dictionary written by John Withals in 1574 which said "Fasting is a great remedie of feuer." Nobody knows when and where the saying originated but some sources claim that the proverb really means "If you feed a cold now, you'll have to starve a fever later."

In the past a folk understanding of disease may have seen a distinction between illnesses caused by low temperatures (colds and chills) and those associated with fever and high temperatures. Maybe it was reasoned that feeding someone raises the body temperature while starving it would lower the body temperature.

Until recently doctors and nutritionists rejected the idea as a myth, on the basis that it makes no sense for ill people to weaken their ability to fight infection by either starving or overeating. However, Gijs van den Brink, a cell biologist at the Academic Medical Centre in Amsterdam has conducted studies showing that the balance of two chemicals called cytokines, which form part of the immune system, is affected by eating. He concludes: "There appears to be a parallel between our data and this saying."

Van den Brink found that after a meal the level of the cytokine gamma interferon (INF-y) in the blood of six volunteers increased by 450 per cent. This chemical stimulates the immune system by releasing white blood cells into the bloodstream to destroy infected cells. This immune response fights the viral infections responsible for colds.

Volunteers who were starved showed low levels of INF-y, but four times the level of another cytokine called interleukin-4 (IL-4) which stimulates B-cells to produce antibodies. Antibodies are molecular watchdogs which circulate in the bloodstream looking for viruses, bacteria and other foreign bodies. When they find an unfamiliar object they bind tightly to its surface alerting the other powerful defensive mechanisms available in the immune system. This immune response fights the bacterial infections responsible for most fevers.

According to *New Scientist*, "Van den Brink speculates that the immune response that follows eating evolved as an energy-saving ploy. Whereas most bacterial infections (fevers) need an immediate response, he says, tackling a virus (cold) to which we have already been exposed can wait until we have more energy."

> Verdict

"Evidence that food may have a fleeting effect on a person's immune status is interesting" (van den Brink) but a larger-scale study is required before any conclusions can be drawn.

"Eating cheese before bedtime causes nightmares"

/No one knows for certain where the link between eating cheese and nightmares began, but a strong contender is Charles Dickens' character Ebenezer Scrooge who blamed his nocturnal ghostly visitations on "a crumb of cheese". The link was probably reinforced during the 1950s when it was discovered that eating cheese while on certain early antidepressant medications caused a racing heart rate and dangerously high blood pressure.

Tryptophan and Tyramine
Cheese contains the amino acid tryptophan, which in the body induces the release of serotonin, a neurotransmitter which contributes to feelings of well-being and happiness and aids sleep. In fact, tryptophan in turkey is often mistakenly cited as a cause of post-Christmas dinner drowsiness, when carbohydrates are the real culprit and levels of tryptophan in all foods are too low to cause drowsiness. However, cheese also contains the amino acid tyramine, which induces the release of noradrenaline, often called the "fight or flight" chemical, as it is responsible for the body's reaction to stress. Combining these two ingredients leads to more effective sleep with more vivid dreams.

British Cheese Board

Fortunately, scientists from the knowingly named British Cheese Board conducted the world's first cheese-dream study in 2005 which found that cheese (or at least, the six British cheeses they tested) did not encourage nightmares, but they did find a link between specific cheeses and the content of the test subjects' dreams.

Dream maker

Two hundred volunteers (100 men and 100 women) were given a 20g piece of cheese 30 minutes before bedtime and recorded their dream experiences for a week. Seventy-five per cent of the subjects reported having a good night's sleep and two-thirds of them were able to recall their dreams.

Subjects who ate Stilton reported the most unusual dreams including a maudlin vegetarian crocodile which couldn't eat children and soldiers fighting with kittens instead of bullets.

Red Leicester elicited nostalgic dreams in sixty per cent of participants and was the most effective at encouraging a good night's sleep. Celebrities from Jordan to Johnny Depp appeared in sixty-five per cent of the dreams of people who ate Cheddar, while two-thirds of consumers of Lancashire cheese experienced work-related dreams.

British Brie caused predominantly pleasant dreams for females and quirky obscure dreams for males which included having a drunken conversation with a dog, while over a half of Cheshire eaters reported refreshing but completely dreamless sleep.

>Verdict

Eating a little cheese before bedtime aids sleep and makes dreams more vivid, but it does not cause nightmares.

"Throw back the first fish you catch, then you'll be lucky the whole day fishing"

/ If you are freshwater fishing then catch-and-release is good for fish stocks and helps to ensure that next month there will be fish to catch. If you are sea fishing, the ocean is so vast that a single fish thrown back won't make much difference. Can throwing back your first fish really affect the chances of catching more fish in a single day or is it simply an old tradition of thanking the sea gods for your good fortune by offering up the first fruits?

Food for the gods

Just about every ancient culture made offerings to its gods, especially of food. For example, the Māori people of New Zealand believed that cultivation and collection of food was under the jurisdiction of a different *atua* or god and the first fruits were always reserved for them. Fishermen would throw back the first catch as a *karakia* (prayer) for *Tangaroa*, the god of the sea. A Māori legend tells of Manuruhi who caught a fish without making this offering and Tangaroa became so angry that he turned him into a *tekoteko* (carved human form/statue) on top of his *wharenui* (sacred meeting house).

If you have no gods to appease, returning a fish to the water can be good or bad depending on whether the fish is dead or alive, thrown or placed.

Place not throw

First off, throwing anything into the water is always bad. When river fishing any object splashing into the water scares other fish away and the noise of the splash can carry for long distances. Live fish must be placed into the water, not thrown, otherwise they will be injured. You should get down close to the water and let the fish swim from your hands. If the fish is exhausted from being reeled in, you may even have to hold the fish in the water facing the current until it has regained its strength.

Hold your breath

Removing the hook quickly and correctly is also important. The longer you take the more you stress the fish and the smaller its chance of survival. Keep the fish out of water for no longer than the length of time you can hold your breath. If you must handle the fish make sure your hands are wet to avoid damaging the protective layer of mucus on its skin.

Spreading disease

Throwing dead fish into fresh water is usually to be discouraged. It provides a free lunch for other water creatures, but in many areas anglers are advised to take dead fish, fish parts and unused bait home to avoid risking the spread of invasive species and diseases in the water, which are the largest cause of biodiversity loss in lakes around the world (in the US the most well-known are the zebra mussel and the Asian Carp).

Cut bait

The only way to increase your chances of catching fish during the day is to chop up your first fish and throw a handful in the water to attract other fish – but not too much. You don't want them to grab a snack and then leave because they are too full to take your hook.

When fishing in sea water and at depths of more than thirty feet there's little point in throwing back your fish because being forced to the surface quickly on the end of your line will kill it anyway, in the same way that a scuba diver gets the bends.

>Verdict

Throwing back the first catch of the day will not improve your luck and may even scare other fish away.

17

"If you swim within an hour of eating you will get cramp "

/Swimming immediately after eating is not the death sentence that we have all been led to believe. What's more puzzling and would make a fascinating study in itself is why people have persisted for so long with this myth, denying themselves a refreshing swim by waiting for an hour after eating, thinking they risk drowning from stomach cramps.

Blood and guts

Digesting food does require a greater circulation of blood towards the gut, leaving less available for your muscles and lungs, but if this were great enough to stop you swimming it would also preclude all forms of physical activity; we'd all have to lie down in a dark room after every meal, which is indeed what happens in many Mediterranean countries in the form of a siesta. But this is also a cultural rather than a medical practice and dictated more by the need to avoid the sun during the hottest time of day than to avoid all physical activity after lunch.

Lazy days

It's curious that we praise the benefits of a Sunday afternoon walk to work off the roast dinner, but as soon as water enters the equation this physical activity becomes something to avoid at all costs.

Lazy parents?

There may be another reason, this time cultural, why this myth has persisted. In swimming pools and on beaches, lifeguards are more common than they were fifty years ago, when parents would need to be extra vigilant to ensure their brood didn't get into trouble in the water. Parents are right to be wary around water – drowning remains one of the leading causes of accidental death in childhood – but drowning caused by stomach cramps just doesn't show up in the figures, even in countries where children aren't advised to stay out of the water after a meal.

Staying alert is hard work and parents need a break, especially when they have just eaten lunch, perhaps with a few glasses of wine, and are feeling sleepy. What better way to avoid the need for vigilance and to catch a quick nap than to tell Junior that he needs to wait for an hour before taking a swim? In Cuba, children are told they must wait three hours after eating to swim, which can only suggest that those parents really value their kick-back time.

>Verdict
You won't win any Olympic medals by swimming directly after a big meal, but there are no documented cases of anyone getting postprandial cramps and drowning.

"The larger the earlobes the greater the intellect"

/Ears feature in several superstitions linking their physical attributes to character or intellect: small ears are supposed to suggest someone of delicate character, thick ears denote someone with a coarse or sensual nature; thin angular ears have been linked with temper and long or prominent ears with musical talent. All nonsense, of course and part of a centuries-old concern with physiognomy, the assessment of a person's character or personality from outer appearance, especially the face.

Physiognomy

This practice can be traced back to the ancient Greeks and the earliest work surviving in Greek on the subject, *Physiognomics,* was probably written a few decades after the death of Aristotle, although even then opinion was divided on whether it was medicine or divination. By the Middle Ages physiognomy was being taught in universities and later, phrenology – measurements of the human skull – became popular too. During the next few centuries physiognomy became a cornerstone of scientific racism and a justification for imperialism and slavery.

Criminology

Detailed physiognomic descriptions of characters appear in the novels of Charles Dickens and Thomas Hardy and one leading nineteenth-century criminologist, Cesare Lombroso, believed he could even detect physiological differences between different types of criminal. His observations led him to conclude that murderers tended to have cold, glassy, blood-shot eyes, curly hair, strong jaws, long ears and thin lips while sex offenders betrayed their inner nature with glinting eyes, strong jaws, thick lips, copious hair and projecting ears.

Hearsay

Modern scientists now dismiss physiognomy as a pseudoscience, which means that there is no link between the genetic size of your earlobes and your intellect. However, there is a link between earlobe size and life experience because noses and ears continue to grow as we age and the earlobes elongate from gravity as collagen and skin elasticity decrease. Age is equated with wisdom in many cultures, especially in Oriental religions, where all enlightened beings are shown to have disproportionately long ears.

Lobe lift

Never one to miss a trick, the beauty industry has been quick to add earlobe size to its list of preventable ageing horrors, so it offers injectable fillers and even surgery called 'earlobe rejuvenation' to make them more rounded, smaller and more youthful in appearance.

>Verdict

There is no link between genetic earlobe size and intellect, but there is a link between earlobe size and life experience because ears grow as we age and lobes sag due to gravity.

"Swallowed chewing gum remains in your stomach for seven years "

/Chewing gum sticks to the pavement for years so it doesn't take much of a mental leap to believe that it can stay in our guts, but this just isn't supported by medical science. Gum may be a persistent nuisance on the floor but it doesn't stick around in your stomach because your digestive system digests what it can and excretes what it can't.

Gummed up

In medical literature there have been a handful of cases of young children developing intestinal blockages from swallowing excessive amounts of gum. David E. Milov's 1998 article "Chewing Gum Bezoars of the Gastrointestinal Tract" in the journal *Pediatrics* points out that "a significant amount of the $21 billion US candy industry sales is from chewing gums, many of which appeal almost exclusively to children. Despite the history and prevalence of gum chewing, the medical literature contains very little information about the adverse effects of chewing gum." His article describes three children who developed intestinal tract and oesophageal obstruction as a consequence of swallowing gum – extreme cases which are not representative of the population at large.

>**CASE 1** was a boy, 4½ years of age with a 2-year history of constipation. He had been eating and swallowing five to seven pieces of gum each day and had to have "a 'taffy-like' trail of faecal material … manually withdrawn" from his rectum which "was primarily made up of chewing gum".

>**CASE 2** was a 4¼-year-old girl with constipation, again caused by being rewarded with several sticks of chewing gum each day, which she was in the habit of swallowing.

>**CASE 3** was a 1½-year-old who had swallowed coins stuck together with chewing gum which were lodged in her oesophagus. Her parents confirmed that she was a regular user of gum (despite her young age).

Milov concluded, "chewing gum should not be swallowed and not given to children who cannot understand this point". Clearly, when very young children swallow large quantities of gum, they develop intestinal obstructions. The risk is much reduced for adults who have wider and larger intestines.

>**Verdict**

In the overwhelming majority of cases, gum swallowed in moderation is usually excreted and does not remain in the stomach. Gum should always be discarded rather than swallowed, but accidentally swallowing gum generally only leads to intestinal problems as a result of excessive consumption.

"Masculine men have longer ring fingers"

/The notion that "masculine men have longer ring fingers" is an excellent example of the way that science can be diluted, misrepresented and framed by inaccurate language. However, hiding inside this vague and misleading statement is a kernel of truth supported by much scientific research. So first, let's be very specific about terminology.

2D:4D ratio

The ratio between the length of the right index and ring fingers (measured from the bottom crease where the finger joins the hand to the tip of the finger) is called the 2D:4D. Numerous studies have found that the 2D:4D is fixed in utero and that it is lower in males than females.

Testosterone

Several scientific studies have shown that the 2D:4D ratio is linked to the amount of testosterone that a foetus is exposed to at the end of the first trimester. So, the greater the difference in length between a man's right ring finger and index finger, the higher was the level of testosterone in utero and the lower the 2D:4D ratio. The lower a man's ratio (i.e. the longer his ring finger relative to his index finger) the more "masculine" he is, if we define masculine as being to the right of an imaginary left/right, female/male continuum.

Facial attraction

Several studies have shown a link between a lower 2D:4D ratio in males and a variety of traits including facial attractiveness. The more masculine the 2D:4D the more attractive the face. High testosterone levels result in attractive traits - the growth of the lower face, jaw, cheekbones, brow ridges - whereas oestrogen inhibits this growth. So the amount of testosterone a man is exposed to in utero contributes to his facial development and attractiveness but it is not the whole story, since testosterone levels at puberty and adulthood also play an important role.

Sports and sexual orientation

Males with lower 2D:4D ratios self-report higher levels of participation in competitive sport than males with higher 2D:4D ratios and there is also a correlation with sexual orientation. Research led by Terrance Williams from the University of California found a lower, more "masculine" 2D:4D ratio in lesbians than in straight women and while that of homosexual men was not significantly different from that of heterosexual men, younger sons (those with at least two older brothers), regardless of sexual orientation, had a significantly more masculine finger ratio than eldest sons. Previous studies have shown that there is a higher proportion of homosexual men among younger sons, so younger sons with a low 2D:4D are statistically more likely to be gay.

>Verdict

The difference in length between a man's right ring finger and index finger is linked to levels of testosterone in utero, facial attractiveness, competitiveness and sexual orientation.

"No one ever sees a dead donkey"

/There is a lot of folklore surrounding donkeys, which is unsurprising as the animal has been closely associated with humans since it was domesticated over five thousand years ago.

Panacea

Christian tradition says that the donkey gained the cross on its back after Jesus rode one into Jerusalem. Various cures have been attributed to the donkey: its right hoof for epilepsy; its milk for tuberculosis, whooping cough and gout; hairs from its back for toothache and to soothe teething babies. However, probably the most well-known piece of donkey folklore is the expression "No one ever sees a dead donkey".

Cynical ass

The expression even crops up in George Orwell's novella, *Animal Farm*. Benjamin the donkey is one of the oldest animals on the farm. When he is asked whether he was happier before or after the Revolution he replies cryptically, "Donkeys live a long time. None of you has ever seen a dead donkey."

Hide and die

Donkeys, in common with many animals such as elephants, have been credited with knowing when they are about to die and going away to die alone. Maybe that is why it was considered good luck to see a dead donkey, since it was such a rarity, and jumping over the carcass of a dead donkey three times was thought to bring good luck. But do donkeys really make themselves scarce before they bite the big one? They are social animals that need companionship for their well-being.

A solitary donkey is an unhappy donkey

Donkeys originated in the African desert and are descendants of the African wild ass. In these desert environments they do not live in close herds like horses or ponies, so they developed the loud characteristic "Eee-aw" sound which can carry over several miles, and large ears to pick up the calls of their companions. In these inhospitable and vast deserts a dead donkey is quickly eaten by scavengers. Many animals seek shelter when they are sick in order to recuperate; if they die in the process then this self-imposed isolation makes them harder to find. Donkeys aren't typical in this respect. However, in wetter climes, donkeys seek shelter because they do not have water-resistant coats like horses, so even a healthy donkey will "hide" under cover when it rains.

Preservation Instinct

As Benjamin pointed out, donkeys live a long time, typically for thirty years or more, and some have even lasted as long as sixty years. They also have a strong preservation instinct so if they consider something to be dangerous they will simply avoid it, unlike horses, which can be trained to jump huge fences or ride into battle.

>Verdict

The paucity of dead donkeys is a well-founded comment on its longevity and preservation instinct rather than its propensity to make itself scarce before dying.

" Sitting too close to the television damages eyesight "

/Parents lie to their children all the time and sometimes they don't even realise they're doing it. Having a child blocking the view of their favourite TV programme is annoying enough to make most parents trot out a half-baked nugget of received wisdom without a second thought. But how can they be sure that sitting close to the television isn't a sign of bad eyesight, or that sitting too far away from the screen and straining to focus doesn't do even more damage?

Fortunately only one of these statements is true: sitting too close to the screen may be a sign that a child is near-sighted and needs glasses, because generally children are better than adults at focusing on things that are close up. This ability declines with age which is why granny has to hold her bodice-ripper at arm's length.

Eye strain

Sitting too close to the television will not damage your eyes permanently but it might cause eye strain. When you view a screen from a distance your eyes only have to move slightly to take in details, but if you watch a large screen up close your eyes have to make large movements to travel from one side of the frame to the other. The most tiring aspect of television viewing is lack of blinking – the more absorbed people become by the screen, the less they blink, so the eyes become dry and itchy – also a common result of staring at a computer screen for long periods without taking regular breaks.

The real problem

The worst thing about television is television itself. Numerous studies have shown a link between hours spent watching television and obesity, aggression, lower language, reading recognition and comprehension skills, poor mathematical ability and sleeping problems. Even more worrying, television presents a distorted and heightened version of reality, and this doesn't just apply to advertising. All content providers from the makers of soap operas to rolling news channels are concerned with viewing figures rather than presenting an objective view of the world.

Symptom, not a cause

So it would appear that the worst effects of television are on the brain. Not according to Marie Evans Schmidt and her team at the Center on Media & Child Health at Children's Hospital Boston. They studied more than 800 youngsters from birth to 3 years and found that the children who spent more time watching television performed worse in language and motor-skill tests at age 3 than those who watched less. But here's where it gets really interesting: when they controlled for other factors like the parents' education and the household income, the link disappeared. This implies that the sort of parents who plonk their kids in front of the telly fail their children in all sorts of other ways, so television is not the cause. Schmidt concluded, "Initially it looked like TV-viewing was associated with cognitive development, but in fact TV-viewing is an outgrowth of other characteristics of the home environment that lead to lower test scores."

>Verdict

Sitting too close to the television does not damage eyesight, but it may cause eye strain or be a sign of near-sightedness.

"Chocolate causes acne"

/Acne has commonly been linked in the public imagination with chocolate, crisps, greasy food, sweets and fizzy drinks. Common sense suggests that a healthy diet produces healthier skin, but scientific research has had varied results and has failed to find a conclusive link between any one single food and acne.

Hundred per cent cacao

Although most scientists agree that chocolate does not cause acne, researchers at the University of Miami Miller School of medicine in Florida found that eating chocolate that was 100 per cent cacao exacerbated acne in individuals who are acne prone. They studied ten healthy males aged between 18 and 35 with a history of facial acne. Each day for a week they were given varying amounts of 100 per cent Ghirardelli chocolate in addition to their normal diet. The results showed a correlation between the amount of acne on Day 1 compared to Day 7. However, eating 100 per cent cacao chocolate is unusual and a randomised placebo-controlled trial with a large sample is needed. All the chocolate available on the high street includes other ingredients such as sugar, emulsifiers, fat and milk solids. Tests involving these more common forms of chocolate have found no link between consumption and acne.

Acne and a healthy GI

Australia's RMIT University and Royal Melbourne Hospital Department of Dermatology spent more than two years studying the relationship between the skin and glucose and insulin levels due to diet. They published their results in the July 2007 issue of the *American Journal of Clinical Nutrition*. Two groups of men aged between 15 and 25 were given contrasting diets for twelve weeks. The first group was allowed to eat sugary drinks and snacks, white bread and potatoes, while the second group ate foods with a low glycaemic index (which release glucose gradually into the bloodstream), including whole grains and high-protein foods. The group eating the healthier GI food showed a fifty per cent reduction in acne compared to the other group. So, as you might expect, there is a link between overall health and consumption of healthy food so anyone who followed a poor diet that included lots of chocolate could expect to have more acne.

The main causes of acne

Acne is caused by a build-up of dead skin cells inside the follicle, plus an excess of sebum. The pore becomes blocked, which creates an anabolic environment for the excessive breeding of the bacteria that cause acne, *Propionibacteria acnes (P.acnes)*. When too much bacteria is present the pore becomes inflamed, creating a papule or zit.

Despite the limited connection between diet and acne, the main triggers are a genetic predisposition towards oily skin (eating fatty food does not cause greasy skin) and levels of androgen hormones such as testosterone. Levels of testosterone increase dramatically during puberty, so acne is more common among teens and male teenagers suffer from worse and longer lasting acne than females. Approximately five per cent of testosterone is converted into dihydrotestosterone, which causes the body to mature during puberty as well as the growth of pubic hair. Dihydrotestosterone also increases the production of skin oil (called sebum) and causes oilier skin.

>Verdict

If you are prone to acne, stay away from pure chocolate, but you can safely enjoy moderate amounts of chocolate as part of a healthy diet.

"Cure a nosebleed with keys down the back"

/Much anecdotal evidence supports this particular home remedy and many doctors will confirm that placing a cold object on a person's back will stop a nosebleed – keys, ice, a cold wet cloth – anything cold enough to shock the body and trigger the mammalian dive reflex, an automated response system for diving in cold water (less than about 21°C/70°F). In fact an even more effective way to achieve the same result is to submerge your face in cold water while holding your breath.

Mammalian dive reflex

The mammalian dive reflex enables mammals to stay under water for extended periods of time by reducing the body's demand for oxygen. As soon as the face makes contact with cold water, receptors in the nasal cavity and around the cranial nerve send a message to the brain which causes bradycardia (the heart slows dramatically) and peripheral vasoconstriction (constriction of blood flow to the extremities). This makes more oxygen available for the vital organs, especially the brain, and means less blood pumping out of your pesky nose.

The dive reflex in aquatic mammals like seals, dolphins and otters is very pronounced, reducing their heartrate by as much as ninety per cent, but in very cold water even humans can experience a seventy-five per cent reduction. The colder the water the more pronounced the diving reflex, which is why a cold object pressed against the back is so effective; the sudden shock fools the autonomic nervous system into responding as if the body had suddenly been submerged in cold water.

Bear Grylls

Survival expert Bear Grylls demonstrated this in Season Five of *Man vs Wild* by swimming beneath the ice in a lake in the Canadian Rockies. His heartrate immediately slowed from 160 to 55 beats per minute. This reflex increases the odds of survival by giving the body vital extra seconds to reach the surface after an accidental submersion or drowning but it will also stop a nosebleed dead in its tracks.

Cold pinch

The most effective treatment for a nosebleed is to combine this cold back technique with a nose pinch. Run the cold object – keys, ice, butter knife – along the person's spine while they sit pinching their nose firmly just below the bridge with their thumb and index finger. Lean the head forward and get the person to breathe through their mouth for ten minutes. Don't tip the head back, as this will allow the blood to flow down their throat instead of out of their nose.

> **Verdict**

Cold keys down the back can help to cure a nosebleed, but should be combined with other techniques such as nose pinching and breathing through the mouth.

"Don't eat the first snow "

/Children love eating snow, with or without a Styrofoam cup and a variety of delicious and brightly coloured syrups, but parents often advise their children to avoid eating the first snow. Are they right to be concerned?

How snow is made

Snow crystals are formed by the freezing of tiny supercooled droplets of water vapour in the clouds. In warmer clouds the water molecules use a tiny piece of dust as an "ice nucleus" around which to form the snowflake; in colder clouds the droplets can freeze without dust. As they stay in the cloud the ice crystals grow by collecting more water molecules on their surface until they become so large that they drop out of the cloud, and if the air below remains cold enough, fall as snow.

Pollution collector

Helen Suh MacIntosh, a professor in environmental health at Harvard University, studies how environmental pollution affects people's health. She considers snow to be "a fairly efficient pollution collector when it is in the air ... once formed, the crystal can continue to grow and can stay in the air for hours before it falls to the ground. It is during this time that the snow crystal can collect or 'scavenge' pollutants that are present in the air." Even freshly fallen snow can contain metals, acids and persistent organic pollutants (POPs) but you'd have to eat bucketfuls to do yourself serious harm.

Second snow

The second snowfall contains a lower level of pollutants simply because it is exposed to less pollutants since the first snowfall collected some of them. However, the levels won't differ very much between the two snowfalls and a single snow cone will contain tiny amounts of environmental pollution – you would breathe in significantly more during the day than you would consume. Levels of pollution differ between urban and rural areas, but unless you live in a heavily industrial area, snow cones in moderation won't do you any harm, no matter which snowfall you use.

Bacteria is the biggest danger

According to the Canada Safety Council, the biggest danger in eating snow is bacteria. The CSC analysed twenty samples of snow from around the world and found that "the bacteria levels were high in all the samples. The most widespread bacteria in all samples proved to be *Pseudomonas syringae* (which causes diseases in tomato and bean plants) . . . neither a good guy nor a bad guy . . . but experts say there is not much cause for worry. The types of bacteria found in the atmosphere, and ultimately in snow, are not human pathogens and don't cause disease."

The CSC advice on snow eating is, "make sure your child does not eat a lot of snow. It also contains particles from ordinary air pollution ... Catching a snowflake on the tongue is OK. Eating snow that's on the ground is not OK."

> **>Verdict**

Snow does contain environmental pollutants but so long as you eat small quantities and avoid dirty brown or yellow snow, you won't do yourself any harm. It is important to keep risks in perspective: the high fructose corn syrup poured liberally over a snow cone is a higher cause for concern.

" Rub a gold ring on a stye "

/**Many people still swear by this centuries-old remedy and while there is no conclusive scientific proof that it works, under certain conditions concentrations of positive ions of some metals including silver, gold, brass and copper do have antibacterial properties known as the "oligodynamic effect".**

Staphylococcus aureus

A stye, which looks like a large pimple on your eyelid, is caused by bacterial infection of the sebaceous glands near the base of the eyelashes, most commonly by *Staphylococcus aureus*. This bacterium is commonly found on the skin and in the nasal passages and can cause pimples and boils as well as styes.

Oligodynamic action

In 1893 a Swiss botanist called Karl Wilhelm von Nägeli discovered and named the "oligodynamic" action of certain metals after observing that algae were killed when placed in water in contact with copper. He found that arsenic, mercury, copper, silver, lead and gold, in descending order of effectiveness, demonstrated oligodynamic action. Nägeli observed that gram-positive organisms were affected more than gram-negative ones (*Staphylococcus aureus* is gram-positive) but his and subsequent studies found that gold was the least effective of these metals. Silver, copper and brass all have greater oligodynamic properties than gold, so if this mechanism plays a part in killing bacteria in a stye, it is curious that gold has taken precedence over these more effective metals.

Sterling work

The antibacterial properties of silver have been well known for centuries. Silver compounds and dressings containing silver sulfadiazine are used to kill bacteria in external wounds and NASA used copper-silver ionisation to make drinking water for the Apollo space programme. Even pioneers in the American West knew that dropping a copper or silver coin in their drinking bottles kept the water fresh for longer. Silver spoons and brass door knobs self-sanitise because of the oligodynamic action. Samsung has even developed a trademarked Silver Nano antibacterial technology which uses silver nanoparticles in washing machines, refrigerators and vacuum cleaners creating an anti-bacterial and sterilisation effect.

However, rubbing a gold ring on your skin is very different to leaving metal submerged in water or using a nano-coating to protect a surface from bacteria. Moisture is present on the skin, so a limited transfer of ions may occur, but it is hard to see how such brief skin contact could generate a significant oligodynamic action.

Treatment

Once you notice that a stye is developing on your eyelid, you should avoid squeezing or rubbing it as this could spread the bacterial infection over the entire eyelid. A staph infection can be treated with antibiotics such as chloramphenicol or amoxicillin, but this is only necessary if the stye persists. Usually you can relieve the symptoms by applying a hot, moist compress (a clean facecloth or towel) for ten minutes, four times a day, which will draw the trapped fluids out of the infected sebaceous gland. Then try rubbing gently with a gold or silver ring – you won't do any harm and may even do some good.

>Verdict

Nobody has proved conclusively that a gold ring can cure a stye using oligodynamic action. If this were the case, then a silver or copper ring should be even more effective, but this remedy may yet prove to be more than an old wives' tale.

" You grow in your sleep "

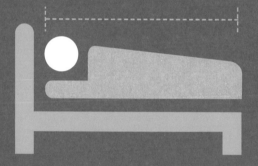

/Children do all their growing while they sleep. Also, when we wake up after a night's sleep we are about one inch taller than when we went to bed.

Anterior pituitary gland

This pea-sized gland is located at the bottom of your brain, behind your eyes and in front of your ears. It synthesises growth hormone, which stimulates growth, cell reproduction and regeneration. It secretes the hormone throughout the day at 3- to 5-hour intervals, but the peak secretion is about one hour after you go to sleep and about fifty per cent of growth hormone secretion occurs during deep sleep (which begins about forty minutes after you fall asleep). People who regularly fail to get enough sleep can experience lower levels of growth hormone.

Sleep and cell repair

Good sleep is important throughout life, because even though adults usually stop gaining height after the age of twenty, they still need to produce about sixty per cent as much growth hormone as children to repair and generate new cells in the body. Despite this, growth hormone production declines with age and one of the main causes is that older people tend to spend less time in deeper sleep phases.

Adults grow every night

The spinal column consists of 33 separate vertebrae – pieces of bone – connected by tough tissue called ligaments which allow a certain amount of flexibility, so your spine can be strong without being rigid. Between each vertebra is a thin intervertebral disc which acts as a cushioning pad and is made of a flexible connective tissue called cartilage, the same material that forms the top of your ear and the front of your nose and is found between the joints of many of your bones.

Cartilage is made up of specialised cells called chondroblasts that produce a large amount of collagen. During the day the intervertebral discs become compressed by gravity as you remain upright and go about your business. The thickness of the intervertebral discs, which account for about a quarter of the length of your spine, reduces as the cartilage becomes depleted of nutrients, so you shrink. During the night the discs absorb nutrients and are allowed to expand again and become plumper because gravity is acting sideways rather than crushing them flat, meaning you wake up an inch taller. For the same reason astronauts often gain two or three inches in height after they have been in zero gravity for an extended period of time, but they lose the height gain when they return to earth.

>Verdict

Only children and adolescents grow in their sleep, but good sleep is important for everyone because growth hormone, secreted mostly during sleep, promotes cell repair.

"Whistling on stage brings bad luck"

/Fifty years ago whistling on stage could have brought you a large dose of bad luck in the form of a piece of scenery landing on your head. Today nearly all scenery rigs are operated by computers or cued through headphones. Whistling backstage during a modern performance or rehearsal would be discouraged anyway because the sound would easily carry onto the stage and could distract the other actors, or be heard by the audience.

Ship shape

Whistling backstage became taboo because theatrical managers used to hire sailors to operate the fly loft, since they were skilled at making knots and working with rigging. Heavy scenery would be cued in and out using a repertoire of whistles, so anyone whistling at the wrong time could spell disaster.

Whistling up a storm

Historically, sailors have had an ambivalent attitude towards whistling. It is considered bad luck to whistle on board ship because it could summon up strong winds (hence the expression "to whistle up a storm") although on naval vessels whistles were used to send orders (e.g. the Bosun would whistle to set the pace for scrubbing the decks) so whistling would have been taboo to avoid confusion and subordination. If a ship was becalmed it was permissible to get a young boy to whistle a tune on deck to bring some wind, because he would not be powerful enough to bring misfortune.

Generation gap

Older British actors still observe the no whistling rule and have to explain it to younger actors who are often unfamiliar with the superstition. West End veteran Michael Ball talked about his superstitions in a 2009 interview in the *Guardian*: "I'm really superstitious . . . I have to suck a sweet at a certain time, have a drink at a certain time, and nobody is allowed to whistle backstage. The last thing my dresser has to say to me is: 'Are we smelling nice for the ladies and gentlemen?'" In a recent appearance on ITV's *Jonathan Ross Show* he talked about how he had to keep throwing Hollywood star Antonio Banderas out of his dressing room for whistling.

The Scottish play

Certain other stage superstitions are more well known and more widely observed than avoidance of whistling, such as referring to Shakespeare's *Macbeth* as "the Scottish play" for fear of bringing bad luck to a show. The customary remedy for whistling or saying "Macbeth" is to walk out of the room, spit, curse, turn round three times and then knock to be let back in.

>Verdict

The avoidance of whistling in a theatre is still a commonly held superstition, especially amongst older actors, although the original reason for this has long since disappeared.

" Eating spicy food causes ulcers "

/For decades doctors believed that ulcers, or peptic ulcer disease (PUD) were caused by stress, spicy foods, smoking, drinking and poor eating habits, but in the 1980s scientists discovered that while spicy food can irritate existing ulcers, it can never cause them.

Gastric ulcers are sores in the mucosal lining of the stomach. Ulcers also appear in the lining of the first part of the small intestine, where they are called duodenal ulcers. They are excruciatingly painful and can cause vomiting and weight loss. When they bleed they cause blood in the stool or vomit and in severe cases they can perforate, which requires surgery to repair the stomach lining.

Triple theory for infection

"Spicy foods, no matter how much you eat, will not cause ulcers," according to Professor Thomas Borody, an Australian gastroenterologist based in Sydney who has made a career pioneering treatments for gastrointestinal disorders. He should know, because in scientific circles he is famous for developing the triple theory for infection with *Helicobacter pylori* bacteria (bismuth, metronidazole and tetracycline) and he has worked closely with Dr Barry Marshall and Dr Robin Warren who received a Nobel Prize for their research showing that *H. pylori* was the real cause of stomach ulcers. A second less common cause of ulcers is the repeated use of non-steroidal anti-inflammatory drugs such as aspirin and ibuprofen although about half of people who develop an ulcer in this way also test positive for *H. pylori* infection.

Marshal and Warren identified the bacterium in 1982 and also found a link between the development of duodenal ulcers and stomach cancer. At the time no one believed that ulcers could be caused by a bacterium so Dr Barry Marshall swallowed some *H. pylori*, developed ulcer-like symptoms and proved their theory. The bacterium is commonly spread through unclean food or water or by mouth-to-mouth contact.

Asymptomatic carriers
Fortunately, although over sixty per cent of people have the bacterium in their stomach, only a few develop symptoms. Ulcers can now be easily diagnosed by swallowing a simple pill. If an ulcer is present it reacts with the pill and can be detected twenty minutes later with a breath test. Then the patient can be given a course of antibiotics, instead of the old treatment which was a surgical operation.

Chilli deterrent
Some research suggests that spicy foods which contain chilli (active ingredient capsaicin) may even help to prevent ulcers by changing the acid balance in the stomach, killing the *H. pylori* bacteria. Spicy food can also fix stomach aches and indigestion, as naturopath Ruth Kendon, Product Research and Development Director of National Herbalists Association of Australia explains: "The stomach burns, protects itself, blood flows, the stomach wall starts repairing itself very quickly and that's why chilli can be used to fix stomach aches and dyspepsia."

▶Verdict

Spicy food cannot cause ulcers and may even prevent them, but it can make existing ulcer pain worse.

" Chicken soup fights a cold "

/Science has only relatively recently proved what your Jewish grandmother has known for centuries: chicken soup fights the symptoms of a cold.

Nasopharyngitis

The common cold (aka nasopharyngitis, rhinopharyngitis, acute coryza) is the most frequent infectious disease in humans and it has been around for millennia. Adults can expect to catch two or three colds each year, but children, whose immune systems have been exposed to fewer colds, can average between six and twelve. Symptoms include a sore throat, cough, runny nose and fever and it usually takes just over a week to make a full recovery. There is no cure for the common cold but there are ways to treat the symptoms, and chicken soup is one of the best.

From nagid to neutrophils

Maimonides, the Jewish doctor and philosopher, recommended chicken soup way back in the twelfth century, but the most widely cited modern study into its effectiveness as a cold medication is by doctors at the University of Nebraska Medical Center, headed by pulmonary specialist Dr Stephen Rennard and published in the medical journal *Chest* in 2000. A home-made recipe and thirteen brands of shop-bought chicken soup were tested and nearly all of them were shown to reduce mucus production in a test tube by inhibiting migration of white blood cells called neutrophils.

Lithuanian grandma's recipe

Rennard's home-made soup was his wife's Lithuanian grandmother's recipe, which contained chicken, onions, sweet potato, parsnips, turnips, carrots, celery, parsley and matzo balls. He tested the soup as a whole as well as the separate components: "all the ingredients were found to be inhibitory, including the boiled extract of chicken alone". Of the commercial brands, "about a third of them were more active than grandma's soup . . . one or two of them had very little activity at all".

Cilia and cysteine

Chicken soup attacks the cold in several ways. It has been shown to improve the function of cilia, the tiny hair-like structures inside the nose that prevent disease from entering the body. Your body produces mucus when disease-fighting neutrophils flood into the nose, throat and lungs to combat infection, causing the sniffles and inflammation (sore throat and congestion). Chicken soup makes mucus more runny, helping you to breathe more easily and speeding up the rate at which you eliminate the virus from your body. It does this more effectively than merely drinking hot water, because it contains an active ingredient called cysteine.

Cysteine is an amino acid with the chemical formula $HO_2CCH(NH_2)CH_2SH$ that is chemically similar to its derivative, acetylcysteine which is used for its mucus-dissolving properties to treat bronchitis. Curiously, cysteine is one of the 600 additives that are added to cigarettes, according to a 1994 report released by five top cigarette companies, possibly to counteract the increased mucus production caused by smoking.

> **Verdict**

Chicken soup fights the symptoms of a cold. Shop-bought soups can be just as effective as your grandma's recipe, but they won't taste as good.

"Forty-five per cent of body heat is lost through the head"

/The next time your granny tells you to wear a hat because you lose nearly half your body heat through your head, tell her she needn't worry because science says that's nonsense. The human head accounts for about ten per cent of the body's surface area and consequently heat loss through the head is about ten per cent, otherwise going outside in the cold without a hat would be as uncomfortable as forgetting your trousers.

Origins of the myth

One source of this adage "was probably based on an infant's head size, which is a much greater percentage of the total body than an adult head," says Dr David Pollack, a senior physician in the Children's Hospital of Philadelphia Care Network. It may also be because the face, head and chest are more sensitive to changes in temperature so you can feel warmer when you cover them up, but one of the main culprits was a flawed temperature experiment conducted by the US military during the 1950s. Subjects were exposed to sub-zero temperatures while wearing Arctic survival suits; since their heads were the only areas of their bodies which were left bare, unsurprisingly they lost most of their heat through their heads. Consequently the advice found its way into army survival manuals.

"Always keep your head covered. You can lose 40 to 45 per cent of body heat from an unprotected head and even more from the unprotected neck, wrist, and ankles. These areas of the body are good radiators of heat and have very little insulating fat.

The brain is very susceptible to cold and can stand the least amount of cooling. Because there is much blood circulation in the head, most of which is on the surface, you can lose heat quickly if you do not cover your head."

FM 21-76 US ARMY SURVIVAL MANUAL
Page 148 Basic principles of
cold weather survival

Body core cooling

Subsequent experiments have found this not to be the case. In March 2006 the paper "Thermal effects of whole head submersion in cold water on nonshivering humans" appeared in the *Journal of Applied Physiology*: "The study isolated the effect of whole head submersion in cold water, on surface heat loss and body core cooling, when the confounding effect of shivering heat production was pharmacologically eliminated."

Eight men were placed in 17°C water in four conditions: body insulated or uninsulated and with head either submerged or above the water. Submersion of the head only increased heat loss by ten per cent, although it increased the rate of cooling by an average of 42 per cent. The scientists proposed this "may be explained by a redistribution of blood flow in response to stimulation of thermosensitive and/or trigeminal receptors in the scalp, neck and face". Submersion of the head reduced core temperature more quickly because scalp blood vessels do not vasoconstrict in response to the cold like other surface vessels do, but total heat loss through the head was proportionate to its surface area.

Heat loss and exercise

When you exercise, heat loss through the head temporarily increases but then falls back down to ten per cent. Your heart pumps faster, blood flow to the brain increases and consequently heat loss increases but, as you continue to exercise, your muscles demand more oxygen and the skin vasodilates, increasing blood flow to the skin to cool the blood and maintain core body temperature. The result is that total heat lost through the head is about ten per cent.

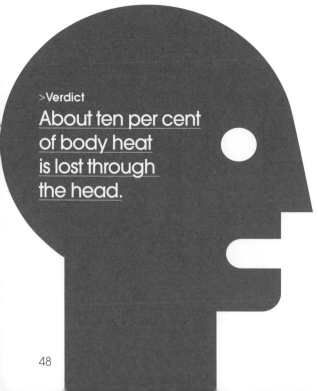

>Verdict

About ten per cent of body heat is lost through the head.

" Seizures are brought on by a full moon "

/Historically, the arrival of a full moon has been associated with werewolves and insanity, and increased levels of crime, accidents, hospital admissions and suicides. An arcane pejorative term to describe the dangerously mentally ill – lunatic – derives from Luna, the Greek word for the moon.

Fluid brains

Philosophers such as Aristotle and Pliny believed that the full moon influenced behaviour, since the tides are affected by the moon and the brain is mostly composed of water. Incidentally, Pliny also believed that epilepsy could be cured by drinking the blood of gladiators, but there is no scientific evidence to support any of these claims, and there is only one small study that has found a link between lunar phases and seizures.

Mistletoe and demons

Four hundred years earlier Hippocrates had recognised that epilepsy ran in families and was a medical condition of the brain, but by the Middle Ages magic and prayer were the most common treatments. Mistletoe also became associated with epilepsy and was hung around children's necks to protect against seizures. By the sixteenth century epileptics were commonly labelled as demonically possessed witches and even during the seventeenth century mistletoe continued to be used to ward off fits during a full moon.

Involuntary and unpredictable

Epileptic seizures are an involuntary and often unpredictable side effect of epilepsy, which is caused by damage to or malformations in the brain in the form of lesions, tumours or head trauma. About two per cent of the population suffer from epilepsy and in most cases, it is controlled by medication.

Greek anomaly

In 2006 a paper headed by P. Polychronopoulus from the Department of Neurology, University of Patras Medical School in Greece was published in the journal *Neurology*. The team reviewed the admission records from its emergency unit over a four-year period: "Overall 859 patients admitted for seizure occurrence were divided into the four quarters of the synodic month according to moon phases. A significant clustering of seizures around the full moon period was observed, supporting the ancient belief of periodic increased seizure frequency during full-moon days."

Disturbed sleep

The paper's authors didn't offer any reasons for this result, although a 1999 article in the *Journal of Affective Disorders* theorised that the phases of the moon may in the past have influenced people with bipolar disorder, since the increase in light during the full moon could have disturbed their sleep. Some types of epilepsy are affected by lack of sleep (for example people with juvenile myoclonic epilepsy can experience problems during the few hours after waking) but this theory presupposes that individuals were incapable of taking compensatory measures.

Chaos theory

This single Greek study appears to support the link between lunar phases and seizures, but even Steven Strogatz, Professor of Applied Mathematics at Cornell University and one of the world's leading researchers into chaos, complexity and synchronisation, advises caution: "...spooky effects have been ascribed to the phases of the moon ... But when the statistics are redone properly, the correlation with lunar phase always evaporates ...Yet many sensible people – including police officers and emergency room staff – continue to believe otherwise."

The future of prediction

Chaos theory is now being used to predict and treat seizures before they occur, explicitly without the help of the moon. Researchers at the University of Florida Brain Institute and the Malcom Randall Veterans Affairs Medical Center in Gainesville have developed a technique using sophisticated mathematical formulae to analyse hours of complex electrical brain signals and discern patterns that previously had appeared to be random.

>Verdict

Despite the results of a single Greek study, there is most likely no link between the lunar phases and seizures. The most promising path to preventative treatment lies in chaos theory, which can rescue us from resorting to medieval superstition to explain life's complexity.

"Sugar makes children hyperactive "

/Numerous studies have shown not only that there is no link between sugar and hyperactivity, but that parents who merely believe that their children have eaten sugar are more likely to report a change in behaviour and to treat them differently as a result. In fact, there are no good scientific studies linking any food to adverse behaviour, let alone sugar.

Feingold exclusion diet

From the 1970s the link between food and behaviour became deeply entrenched after the allergist Dr Benjamin Feingold published his Feingold Exclusion Diet which banished more than 300 food additives and colourings in order to treat hyperactivity. Sugar became caught up by association because many additive-rich foods such as sweets and fizzy drinks also contain a lot of sugar.

Party animals

When children show out-of-control behaviour at family gatherings, parties and other special occasions where sugary food and drinks are abundant, it is common for parents to associate it with those three bowls of ice cream rather than the social environment. However, in 1995 the *Journal of the American Medical Association* published a review of 23 studies conducted during the previous twelve years in which children were generally split into two groups: one were given sugar, the other a placebo. In every study there was no link between sugar and behaviour.

Sugar sensitivity or cognitive rigidity?

One such study was conducted by Daniel Hoover and Richard Milich and the results were published in the article "Effects of sugar ingestion expectancies on mother–child interactions" which appeared in the *Journal of Abnormal Child Psychology* in 1994. Thirty-five children aged 5 to 7 who were reported by their mothers to be "sugar sensitive" were randomly assigned to one of two groups. The mothers in one group were told that their children had been given a large dose of sugar, while the control group mothers were told their children had received a placebo. In fact, all the children had received a placebo.

The mothers in the first group reported higher levels of hyperactivity. They were videotaped interacting with their children which showed that "these mothers exercised more control by maintaining physical closeness, as well as showing trends to criticize, look at, and talk to their sons more than did control mothers". Also, the mothers who most strongly believed that their children were sugar sensitive scored the highest on a test to measure cognitive rigidity (difficulty focusing on more than one stimulus at a time).

>Verdict

Sugar does not affect behaviour, but it does influence the way that parents who believe the myth interact with their children.

"Sage is good for the memory"

/Today sage is mainly used with onion and breadcrumbs to stuff poultry but in times gone by it was considered a wonder remedy for a variety of ailments. It has long been associated with improving memory and now British scientists have conducted clinical trials that support this ancient lore.

The history of sage

The Romans called sage Salvia, which comes from the Latin word salvere, meaning "to be in good health" (the same root as the word salvation). They performed an elaborate ceremony when harvesting it, and considered it an important aid to digestion with sacred properties. The French call sage "Toute Bonne", which means "All Is Well". The Arabs associated sage with immortality and the Chinese used to trade three or four cases of fine tea in exchange for one case of this desirable herb. In 1597 the English herbalist John Gerard published his large and heavily illustrated *Herball, or Generall Historie of Plantes,* which became the most popular botany book in English in the seventeenth century. He wrote that sage "is singularly good for the head and brain and quickeneth the nerves and memory".

The science of sage

In 2003 a team from the Medicinal Plant Research Centre (MPRC) at the Universities of Newcastle and Northumbria published the results of their study of 44 healthy adults aged between 18 and 37. Those who were given daily doses of sage oil performed significantly better than the control group in word recall tests. Lead researcher Nicola Tildesley said: "This proves how valuable the work by the old herbalists is, and that they shouldn't just be ignored because they were writing centuries ago." She also advises caution to students thinking about popping sage pills at exam time: "Tests would need to be carried out on people over a longer period of time to prove that sage improves exam performance, but we don't have any plans to do this at present."

Sage and dementia
Sage is known to reduce inflammation and research has found that Salvia miltiorrhiza, known commonly as Danshen or Chinese sage, contains active compounds similar to those modern drugs already used to treat people with Alzheimer's Disease. Sage is an acetylcholinesterase inhibitor (AChEI) which inhibits the breakdown of the neurotransmitter acetylcholine, which is depleted in dementia sufferers.

Memory aid
In a recent study at the Brain Sciences Institute at Swinburne University in Melbourne, Australia, sage provided cognitive benefits to older adults without dementia. Subjects aged 65 and over were split into four groups and given varying doses of sage: 167mg, 333mg, 666mg and 1,332mg. The 333mg dose resulted in the most significant improvement in memory.

>Verdict
Sage has a range of health benefits which include enhanced memory and word recall.

"Eating your crusts is good for you"

/Eating your crusts won't put hair on your chest but recent research has shown that it can protect against bowel cancer, the third most common form of cancer in the West, and crusts may be healthier than the rest of the bread.

Maillard reaction

Previous studies focused on the health benefits of the fibre which is found in the crust and the crumb, but in 2002 German scientists discovered that the chemical reaction that makes the crust become crispy and brown – the Maillard reaction (named after Louis-Camille Maillard, the chemist who first described it in 1912) – also generates powerful antioxidants from the ingredients.

One of these antioxidants is a cancer-fighting compound called pronyl-lysine and there is eight times more of it in the crust than in the rest of the loaf. This compound, which is not present in the raw ingredients, is created when the protein-bound amino acid L-lysine reacts with starch and reducing sugars during the baking process. The Maillard reaction occurs in both yeast and yeast-free breads but it only takes place on the surface of the bread where the temperature is the highest. In the oven the centre of the bread reaches a temperature of about 100°C because of the water in the dough but this rises to more than 250°C at the crust.

The health benefits of pronyl-lysine
In laboratory studies on human intestinal cells at the Institute of Human Nutrition and Food Science in Kiel, Germany, pronyl-lysine was found to raise levels of phase II enzymes, which have been shown to prevent cancer in earlier studies. More recently, researchers at the Annamalai University in India tested the effects of pronyl-lysine on rats and measured a 72 per cent reduction in pre-cancerous lesions called aberrant cryptic foci (ACFs) in rats fed with a daily portion of bread crusts.

They announced: "Our results provide evidence that continuous exposure to pronyl-lysine significantly reduces the number of ACFs" but further research is needed to find the most beneficial dose in humans, although it is likely that a daily portion of crusts is required for maximum benefit.

Coffee and toast
So, does toasting bread make it more nutritious? Yes, because the toaster is hot enough to create the Maillard reaction. The same process releases antioxidants from the proteins in coffee beans when they are roasted, turning them a dark brown and packing them with a rich complex flavour. However, beware of burnt toast because research has linked this to an increased risk of cancer.

>Verdict
Eating your crusts daily is good for you and toast is healthier than bread, so long as it isn't burnt.

"Sucking your thumb ruins your teeth"

/Babies and young children have a natural urge to suck their thumbs. Thumb-sucking even takes place in the womb but children who continue the habit beyond the age of six and after the arrival of their adult teeth run the risk of damaging them as well as the roof of their mouth.

Buck teeth

About eighty per cent of infants suck their thumbs. It provides comfort, especially during times of stress or when the child is tired, and it can aid sleep. Prolonged thumb-sucking can push the front teeth forward so that they form a malocclusion – the teeth become misaligned. If the teeth are pushed forward too far they can even cause damage to the upper palate. The most common result of excessive thumb-sucking is buck teeth, where the top front teeth splay forward and away from each other.

Gentle sucking is less harmful

The intensity of the sucking action is a significant factor in whether it causes damage to the teeth. Some children find comfort merely from placing their thumb or finger in their mouth but do not suck hard. If the digit makes a popping noise when it is removed from the mouth it indicates a strong sucking action which could lead to tooth damage beyond the age of six.

Abnormal bite patterns

In 2002 the *Journal of the American Dental Association* published results of a study led by Dr John J. Warren of the University of Iowa College of Dentistry. He and his team examined 372 children and showed that abnormal changes in bite patterns were most prevalent in children who sucked their thumb beyond the age of four and they reported potential problems in much younger children as well.

Speech disorders

A study led by Clarita Barbosa for the Corporacion de Rehabilitacion Club De Leones Cruz del Sur and the University of Washington Multidisciplinary International Research Training Program indicates that infants who sucked their fingers, or used a pacifier for more than three years, were three times more likely to develop speech disorders. A group of 128 three- to five-year-old pre-schoolers from Patagonia, Chile were examined and the results were published in the open access journal *BMC Pediatrics* in 2009: "These results suggest extended use of sucking outside of breast-feeding may have detrimental effects on speech development in young children."

Majority of children stop naturally

Despite this, most specialists agree that children shouldn't be pressured to stop thumb-sucking before the age of five, because the majority of children stop naturally with no lasting damage to their teeth. About fifteen per cent of children continue to thumb-suck beyond the age of five; they should be gently encouraged to stop, using positive reinforcement techniques, lots of praise and rewards, without causing anxiety or embarrassment.

>Verdict

Thumb-sucking beyond the age of five can damage the teeth and should be gently discouraged.

"Never mix whisky and raw oysters"

/No one knows the origin of this old wives' tale, but the justification appears to be fairly consistent – raw oysters are supposed to harden in your stomach and turn to stone when mixed with whisky. This is untrue. There is nothing unique to whisky and its brewing process to make this happen and many chefs and whisky connoisseurs believe that whisky and oysters are a perfect pairing.

Ask the experts

The Scotch Whisky Association (SWA) is the trade association for the Scotch Whisky industry. Its 56 members account for more than 90 per cent of production and sales of Scotch Whisky. Its website FAQ gives short shrift to the question "Can you drink whisky with oysters or other shellfish?" with the answer: "Yes. It is an old superstition that whisky cannot be drunk with oysters or other shellfish."

The Murder Trust

In the past the myth was so established that during the 1920s a group of five men, later dubbed "the Murder Trust" by the newspapers, actually fed a man whisky and oysters believing it would kill him so that they could commit life-insurance fraud. Their victim was Michael Malloy, a homeless Irishman from County Donegal who was living in New York City and has since become synonymous with being indestructible after surviving several murder attempts by the gang.

One of the men owned a speakeasy and he gave Malloy an unlimited bar tab in the hope that he would drink himself to death. When this failed they poured antifreeze, turpentine, horse liniment and even rat poison into his drinks and still "Iron Mike" survived. Finally they tried raw oysters soaked in methanol because one of the men claimed to have seen a man die after eating oysters and whisky. After this failed they staged a hit and run which hospitalised him. When he was discharged from hospital a month later they gassed him to death by sticking a hose in his mouth. The five men were put on trial: four were executed in the electric chair at Sing Sing prison and the other was sent to prison.

"Sinful indulgement"

Many fine restaurants pair whisky and oysters. The Whisky Bar on Changkat Bukit Bintang in Kuala Lumpur, Malaysia recommends Chocolate, Oyster and Whisky: "The flavours can work harmoniously; pair a fresh oyster with a mouthful of smoky whisky and the most extraordinary flavour explosion occurs. The whisky takes some of the fishiness out of the oyster and the creamy oyster tones down the fieriness of the whisky – a perfect symbiosis. For a sinful indulgement (sic) – high quality chocolate and a good quality whisky. Put them together... what's not to love?"

>Verdict

Raw oysters and whisky is considered a delicacy and is not harmful. If you are in doubt, a personal experiment will give you all the proof you need.

"Going outside with wet hair causes a cold"

/In a recent survey, forty per cent of mothers said they believed that sending their kids out in the cold weather with a wet head would make them ill. Going outside with wet hair may make you colder (evaporation produces cooling thanks to the Second Law of Thermodynamics) but it won't make you catch a cold or flu because those illnesses are caused by one of several viruses that infect the upper respiratory system.

The common cold

Common cold symptoms usually appear between one and three days after infection by one of more than 200 viruses. The first things a cold sufferer notices are often a sore throat and runny nose, but the virus itself doesn't make them feel ill, it's their body's immune response. The accompanying headaches and blocked nose are triggered by white blood cells and chemical messengers released by the body's natural defences in response to the virus.

How to catch a cold

The most frequent way to catch a cold virus is by inhaling airborne viral particles from the cough or sneeze of an infected person, or touching a surface contaminated with a cold virus, such as a door knob, telephone, elevator button or badly washed coffee mug and then passing this infection to your mouth or nose.

>Anthrax chickens

The cold and wet myth was popularised by the research of the French chemist Louis Pasteur. In 1878 he exposed a bunch of chickens to anthrax and found that even though they were naturally immune to the disease, they succumbed and died if they were chilled in a basin of icy water. He repeated the experiment and found that chickens were able to fight the infection if they were wrapped in a warm blanket after their dip.

>Wet trenches

Pasteur's experiments established a link between body temperature and infection that was reinforced by the experience of soldiers during the First World War. A German scientist found that soldiers stationed in wet trenches for 72 hours were four times more likely to catch a cold than those who remained in their barracks. However, after the Second World War, researchers in Chicago and the Common Cold Research Unit in Salisbury, England conducted experiments in which volunteers were exposed to mucus infected with the cold virus and also made to wear wet clothes and they showed no increased risk of catching a cold.

>Humidity

We now know that humidity is a more important factor than the cold weather. Many viruses are seasonal but rhinoviruses cause colds mostly in the spring and the autumn when people spend more time indoors infecting each other and when the humidity is at its highest.

>Immune response

When scientists discovered that the common cold was caused by a virus, many more experiments examined the effects of cold on the immune system. Animals exposed to extreme cold have been found to have weakened immune systems, but scientists disagree on whether this is caused by the cold itself or stress and fear. Furthermore, in 1999 Canadian researchers exposed a group of young men to extreme cold for two hours and found it improved their immune response. Also many cold water swimmers extol the health benefits of regular icy dips.

>How to avoid catching a cold

Reduce your risk of catching a cold by washing your hands regularly, especially before eating, and wearing a face mask in confined spaces such as public transport. Stay away from crowds of people during the cold and flu season. If you share mugs, make sure they are washed properly. Better still, bring your own mug into work and don't let anyone else use it.

>Verdict

Even going outside with soaking wet clothes won't increase your risk of catching a cold, let alone wet hair.

"Shaved hair grows back thicker, darker, more quickly and stronger"

/Shaving hair, whether on the head, face, legs or underarms, does not change its thickness, colour or speed of growth but there is some evidence that shaving the head can encourage blood flow to the scalp, which is good for your hair. Numerous studies dating back to 1928 have proved that shaved hair re-grows unchanged.

Cut across the shaft

Long hair can feel soft and thin because the hair shaft tapers at the end. Shaving cuts hair across the shaft, so hair may feel coarse and stubbly, but this is only because it has been cut straight across to reveal the thicker part of the shaft. As the hair grows it tapers again and begins to feel softer and thinner. As stubble regrows it only appears darker because the little dots of growth are contrasted against the lighter skin colour. The rate of growth is controlled by the follicles just underneath the skin, and is not affected by shaving.

Because the hair is all the same length when it re-grows this also gives the illusion that it is thicker and darker. Also new hair has not had the chance to be lightened by the sun.

Out of sight
The growing and pigmentation of the hair shaft takes place in the follicle which is hidden below the skin, so by the time the hair reaches the surface and become visible it is already dead and its pigment and thickness is fixed. Unlike shaving, waxing does affect the hair growth because it damages the follicles so the re-growth can be thinner and lighter.

Natural body changes
The misconception about rate of growth and colour change may have come about because when adolescents begin shaving during puberty the hair growth is less and increases as they reach the later stages of puberty, making them think that it was the shaving that caused the increase in growth rather than natural body changes.

Hair also becomes darker during puberty, but again this is not caused by shaving.

Stubble is stiff
A tree branch or bamboo shoot seems soft and pliable when long, but as soon as you cut it back it becomes stronger and more rigid, although no physical change has taken place other than the cutting.

If hair really did grow back thicker, darker and more quickly after shaving then all men would have bushy beards and bald men would shave their heads to encourage re-growth rather than spend millions on expensive hair care products and implants.

>Verdict

Shaving hair does not alter its growth in any way because it is already dead when it is cut, but as it re-grows it can give the illusion that it is thicker, darker and growing more quickly.

"Knuckle cracking leads to arthritis"

/The word "cracking" carries associations of injury, breakage and damage, so it is to be expected that people have come to associate knuckle cracking with conditions such as arthritis. In fact, joint cracking does not lead to arthritis, but studies have shown that it can damage tendons and ligaments by repeatedly overstretching them, cause swelling and reduce grip strength.

Anatomy of a joint

Joints are the places where two bones meet and articulate. The ends of the bone are covered with cartilage which acts like a cushion and the bones are joined by ligaments. The joint is also surrounded by the capsule, a tough fibrous sleeve that stops it from moving too much. The capsule contains thick synovial fluid which lubricates the joint and nourishes the cartilage. The muscles are attached to the bones by tendons and as the muscles expand and contract they make the joint bend, straighten or rotate.

Cavitation

The synovial fluid has gases dissolved in it – oxygen, nitrogen and carbon dioxide – and when the joint is "cracked" the rapid change of pressure within the joint creates a bubble or cavity, and some of the nitrogen and carbon dioxide escapes quickly, making a cracking sound. The technical name for this process is cavitation – the formation and then the immediate implosion of cavities (bubbles) within a liquid.

Fifty-year experiment

Several scientific studies have shown that cracking knuckles does not cause arthritis. One study examined radiographs of 215 people aged between 50 and 89 and found no increased damage in those of the knuckle crackers. The most famous study had a sample size of just one person – Dr Donald Unger, who was awarded the Ig Nobel Prize for Medicine in 2009 after deliberately cracking the knuckles of his left hand at least twice a day for fifty years but never cracking those on his right hand. After a childhood spent being repeatedly warned by his mother and several aunts that cracking knuckles would cause arthritis, he decided to spend half a century testing their hypothesis. Finally he declared his results: "There was

no arthritis in either hand, and no apparent differences between the two hands" and concluded that "there is no apparent relationship between knuckle cracking and the subsequent development of arthritis of the fingers".

Rand Corporation statistician John Adams subsequently pointed out, with tongue firmly in cheek, a fatal flaw in Unger's methodology: "it appears that the study was not blinded. Blinding would only be possible if the investigator didn't know left from right. This is not likely since studies indicate that only 31 per cent of primary care physicians don't know left from right."

>Verdict

There is no proven link between knuckle cracking and arthritis, but it can cause other injuries such as dislocation or damaged ligaments.

"Morning sickness means a girl is more likely"

/Many old wives' tales, from the shape of the bump to the craving for sweet or sour food, claim to predict a baby's sex. Several studies have shown that chronic morning sickness brings an increased chance of having a girl and one study suggests that the baby may be more intelligent too.

Hospital admissions

In a recent study at the University of Washington, scientists compared the gender outcomes of 2,100 pregnant women admitted to hospital with severe morning sickness during their first trimester with a control group of 9,783 women who did not get severely sick. They found that the hospitalised women were more likely to have girls and that the sickest – hospitalised for three or more days – had an 80 per cent increase in girls compared to the control group.

Another study in Sweden in 1999 analysed 8,186 women who were admitted to hospital for morning sickness and found that 44.3 per cent of them had boys, when the figure for the general population was 51.4 per cent.

Causes of morning sickness

The precise causes of morning sickness are unknown but many scientists believe that hormone levels are responsible and that women carrying girls have a higher level of human Chorionic Gonadotrophin (hCG), which is the same chemical that is measured by home pregnancy tests to confirm a pregnancy.

Healthy signs

About four in five expectant mothers suffer from morning sickness and though unpleasant for the mother, it is usually a sign that the baby is developing healthily. Nausea has also been linked to a lower risk of heart problems and a lower level of miscarriage.

Morning sickness means smarter babies

Some studies indicate that morning sickness is a sign of a higher baby IQ. Researchers at the Hospital for Sick Children in Toronto followed 121 women and measured the IQ of their children at ages three and seven. They found that the children of mothers who suffered from morning sickness were more likely to have higher IQs than those of women who reported no sickness and also tended to score more highly for verbal fluency and simple maths, even when other factors such as the mother's IQ and social background were factored in. The main flaw with the study is that the women were asked to recall how sick they had been several months after the event, so it is possible that the more intelligent women had better recall.

> **Verdict**

Severe morning sickness requiring hospitalisation during the first trimester is linked to a significantly increased chance of a baby girl.

"Crossing your legs gives you varicose veins"

/ Varicose veins can be itchy and unsightly and sometimes they can cause complications such as eczema or ulcers, but they are not caused or made worse by crossing your legs.

Circulatory system

When you take a breath, oxygen enters your lungs where it is transferred into your blood and carried around the body by arteries and tiny blood vessels called capillaries. Then the veins carry deoxygenated blueish blood back to the heart and lungs, where it can collect more oxygen. The veins have one-way valves to stop blood from flowing back the wrong way, and when these and the vein walls become weakened, blood pools in the extremities, especially the legs, and the purple-blue veins swell up.

Overstretched rubber band

Increased pressure in the vein is not the single cause – increased pressure against the flow of blood makes them worse once they begin to form. At one time crossing the legs was thought to make this backpressure worse by acting like a tourniquet and hampering blood flow as the vein carries deoxygenated blood back to the heart, but this is not the case. Healthy veins normally have very elastic walls, but they lose their elasticity when they become weak, like an overstretched rubber band. They become twisted because they are too big to fit into their original space.

Risk factors

More than a dozen studies have examined risk factors for varicose veins and none of them linked them to leg-crossing. Risk factors include genetics, old age, obesity and pregnancy. Smoking, high blood pressure and wearing high heels are not causes but standing for long periods can make them worse. Regular exercise can help to reduce the risk by contracting the muscles around the veins.

Many other vein problems are related to varicose veins but they are also unrelated to leg-crossing – see your doctor if you are concerned. These include haemorrhoids (see page 98), telangiectasias (small clusters of blood vessels on the upper body, especially the face), spider veins (swollen capillaries) and varicoceles (varicose veins in the scrotum).

Treatment

Treatment usually involves closing off the vein surgically; other veins then compensate for the lost vein, so the health implications are minimal. Varicose veins aren't particularly dangerous although they can cause mild swelling of the ankles and feet, pain and "heavy" legs, itching, dermatitis, blood clots and ulcers.

> **Verdict**

Several studies have shown that varicose veins are not caused by sitting with crossed legs.

"Bananas ripen more slowly when separated from the bunch"

/Bananas are notoriously difficult to store. If you put them in the refrigerator they keep but the skins turn brown, but if you leave them in a bunch the last ones you eat may be overripe. The solution is to buy several bananas at different stages of ripeness (yellow for eating, green for storing) and keep any bananas you want to ripen together and separate any you want to stop from ripening any more.

Ethylene

The reason this little trick works is that bananas emit ethylene, a colourless gas (with the formula C_2H_4) with a sweet and musky smell, which speeds up the ripening process, so the more bananas you keep together, the more ethylene they will be exposed to and the quicker they will ripen.

Commercial use of ethylene

Banana suppliers use ethylene to control the rate of ripening on a vast scale. Bananas are harvested when they are green and unripe, transported thousands of miles, then kept in vast warehouses that are divided into different sections, so that the suppliers can pump in ethylene gas to ripen however many batches are needed for sale. If demand is slow, they can slow the ripening process by getting rid of the gas. Unfortunately this does have an effect on the taste. Some suppliers still sell un-gassed bananas, which are reputed to taste better.

Ethylene is flammable, but the small amounts that your bananas produce do not pose a fire hazard. It has also been used as an anaesthetic, and many geologists and classical scholars believe that the famous Greek Oracle at Delphi achieved her trance-like state because of ethylene rising from the ground.

Apples and pears

Other fruits, including pears, apples and tomatoes, produce ethylene as they ripen, so if you kept a banana and an apple in a bag together they would both ripen more quickly than alone. If you want to slow down ripening, keep bananas in the fridge – the skins turn brown but the fruit inside stays fresh. Never put unripe bananas in the fridge as this will affect the taste. Avoid buying bananas with brown skin as this is a sign that they have been stored in a fridge for a long time before shipping. Buy smaller bunches during the summer, as the bananas will ripen more quickly during warm weather.

>Verdict

Bananas ripen more slowly when separated from the bunch, kept away from tomatoes, apples and pears and stored in the fridge.

"Beer before liquor, never sicker; liquor before beer, never fear"

/Many drinkers young and old follow this unwritten rule in one of its various forms, which include "wine before liquor, never sicker" and "never mix grape and grain". The maxim implies that somehow the order of consumption generates different chemical processes within a person's body, affecting the hangover the morning after. However, most scientists agree that only the amount of alcohol you consume affects levels of inebriation (and the subsequent hangover), not the order in which you consume your tipples. So the saying can only hold true if it affects the total amount of alcohol consumed. For this reason alone, in some scenarios liquor before beer can reduce consumption.

Here are three scenarios, with two drinkers of the same sex (Adam and Brad), same build and genetic ability to process alcohol. They each buy five rounds:

Monday

Adam drinks five single gin and tonics (1 unit each) followed by five pints of strong lager (3 units each). Brad drinks ten pints of strong lager. By the end of the evening's binge Adam will have consumed 20 units of alcohol while Brad will have glugged 30 units. Brad is going to feel much worse than Adam in the morning but blames overindulgence rather than mixing his drinks, although he notices that Adam seems none the worse for mixing his drinks in the "correct" order.

Wednesday

Adam drinks five single gin and tonics (1 unit each) followed by five pints of strong lager (3 units each). Brad drinks five pints of strong lager so that by the time he switches to shorts he's already had fifteen units and his judgement is impaired. He orders three doubles and two triples, ending the evening with 27 units. In the morning Brad feels rotten and blames it on drinking beer before liquor. He promises himself that next time he will drink like Adam.

Friday

Remembering how bad he felt last time he had beer before liquor, Brad drinks five single gin and tonics (1 unit each) followed by five pints of strong lager (3 units each). Adam drinks five pints of strong lager followed by five single gin and tonics. By the end of the evening's binge they have consumed 20 units of alcohol each and wake up with similar hangovers. On Saturday morning Brad feels the best he's felt all week but instead of attributing this to a lie in (no work) and the fact that he had much less alcohol than on Monday and Wednesday, he

decides that liquor before beer is the way forward.

Just drink less

See how easy it is for anecdotal evidence to make people change their habits? If you want to reduce your hangover, simply drink less alcohol and stick to light-coloured drinks because there is evidence that certain drinks – those which contain congeners – give you a bigger hangover. Congeners are toxic chemicals that are created during fermentation and darker drinks contain more of them than lighter or clear ones. So if you stick to light-coloured drinks you should feel better in the morning than if you drank the same amount of dark-coloured drinks. For example, whisky has four times more congeners than gin, red wine has more congeners than white wine, bourbon has thirty times more congeners than vodka. A rough descending scale of hangovers from congeners are brandy, red wine, rum, whisky, white wine, gin, vodka, water.

>Verdict

There is no evidence that drinking in a particular order affects how you feel the morning after.

Standing on your head after sex can help you get pregnant

/If sperm found it significantly more difficult to swim upstream against the force of gravity then you have to ask why human beings evolved into bipeds, since walking around on all fours would have conferred a reproductive advantage.

Lying down improves conception

However, most fertility experts recommend that women lie down horizontally for at least fifteen minutes following sex; some even suggest giving nature a helping hand by propping a pillow under the hips, but there is no evidence that going to the extreme and standing on your head gives any additional advantage, especially since using a pillow is more comfortable and probably just as effective.

Fertility treatment studies have found that women who lie on their back for fifteen minutes after intrauterine insemination (IUI) had a 27 per cent pregnancy rate after three cycles and women who stood upright after treatment had an 18 per cent pregnancy rate after three cycles. Remaining horizontal does make a difference, so maybe gravity does come into play.

Conception depends upon a number of factors

Some sexual positions are thought to be more conducive to conceiving than others. The missionary position (woman lying down, man on top) is supposed to give the greatest chance of conception, but there aren't enough scientific studies to back this up. The truth is that there are lots of factors that affect conception: time in the cycle, diet, stress levels, the age of the woman, frequency of sex, being underweight or overweight, smoking and drinking, hot baths (see page 96), over-exercising, the list goes on and on. "Many people think that human reproduction is a much more efficient process than it really is," agrees Dr Robert Stillman, medical director of Shady Grove Fertility Centers in the Washington, DC, area, "... remaining supine for a couple of minutes is more than adequate".

Controlling stress

Standing on your head after sex is probably less beneficial than taking up yoga to reduce stress, tone up the body and improve oxygenation. Controlling stress levels goes a long way to optimise fertility, so rather than rush into sirsasana (headstand) immediately after sex, take a more holistic approach and find a good teacher who can guide you towards a much greater range of benefits. The supported headstand is an advanced pose in yoga and it is necessary to build the muscles in the spine and neck before attempting it.

>Verdict

Standing on your head after sex is probably not worth the effort and is unsupported by medical science.

"Using re-boiled water spoils the tea"

/Few would deny that making the perfect cup of tea is a tricky business. You must first warm the pot, use fresh tea leaves, pour on fresh boiling water, allow to brew for a few minutes and then comes the question of the milk – added before or after the tea. Water tastes best when it is oxygenated. Re-boiling water deoxygenates it further so it contains less oxygen than water that has boiled only once.

Fresh cold water

When filling the kettle, empty out the old water, allow the tap to run for a few seconds and fill with fresh cold water. Purists like to leave the tap running for several minutes but if everyone in the country did this before filling the kettle, hose-pipe bans would be an annual occurrence.

Vital ingredients

Some people prefer to use bottled water because it doesn't have chlorine added to it like tap water does. However, if you like your water with plenty of oxygen use the cold tap because the agitation as it comes out helps to oxygenate the water more than being kept in a bottle. Don't take a shortcut and use water from the hot tap because not only does it contain impurities from the hot water tank, it also lacks that vital ingredient – oxygen.

Soft water is best for tea. Hard water can leave a film floating on the surface, the result of a reaction between the flavonoids in the tea and calcium hydroxide in the water.

Speciality teas

Some speciality teas such as black and oolong should be brewed with water than has almost boiled, or has sat for 30 seconds after boiling, as water above 212°F is said to burn the leaves.

Storing tea

When it comes to storing tea, oxygen is the enemy. Tea should be kept in an airtight container because oxygen oxidises ascorbic acid, catechins and lipids that are present in green tea and affects the taste and its health benefits. Even tea that has been stored correctly loses its freshness after about six months, so throw out any tea that you bought longer than six months ago.

>Verdict

For a perfect cuppa, use water that has only boiled once.

" Eat onions to avoid a hangover "

/Scientists still don't have a cure for a hangover. The body needs at least twenty-four hours to flush out the toxins and replace the fluids, nutrients and electrolytes lost during a drinking binge, but you can take some measures to reduce the discomfort. One of them involves onions. Onion juice is also cited as a hangover cure, with the additional advantage of replacing fluids.

Every culture has a preferred food that is said to reduce the effects of a hangover: the Dutch and Germans favour pickled herring, Mexicans use chillies, Russians drink beetroot soup (borsch) and the onion remedy is popular in France. Parisian market workers and peasants used to end an evening of heavy drinking with a bowl of onion soup, which is easily digestible and contains several important nutrients.

Temporary distraction
Pickled or raw onions have a sharp taste which can temporarily distract your attention away from your headache, upset stomach and muscle fatigue.

Blood sugar boost

Onions are said to boost blood sugar levels and also contain high levels of potassium which is required for proper nerve and muscle function but is lost through excessive urination while drinking. Onions also contain sulphur which is thought to help to purify the liver (amino acid sulphoxides are what make you cry while chopping an onion). They also contain several anti-inflammatory and antioxidant compounds such as quercetin and phenols which may reduce the headache and muscle aches.

>Verdict
Nothing can cure or avert a hangover better than drinking in moderation but onions can help to alleviate some of the consequences of over-indulgence.

81

"Rubbing half a lime on your forehead cures a headache"

/A headache is a pain in the head or upper neck. It is one of the most common sources of pain in the body but it has many causes. Many people claim to have cured their headaches by rubbing half a lime on the forehead, so it definitely works for some, even if is a placebo effect, and there are a few good reasons why you could expect this remedy to alleviate certain types of headache.

Types of headache
There are three major categories of headaches: primary, secondary and cranial neuralgias. Tension headaches are the most common type of primary headache and most adults will have experienced them at some time during their lives. They are also more common in women than men. The next most common primary headache is migraine. Secondary headaches

are the result of some other problem in the head or neck, such as bleeding in the brain, a brain tumour or an infection like meningitis. Cranial neuralgias are caused by inflammation of the nerves in the head and upper neck.

Limes for tension headaches

Rubbing half a lime on your forehead will probably only treat tension headaches, since the other types are more severe and often have a separate underlying cause. If this remedy doesn't work for you this doesn't mean that your headache has a serious cause, although if symptoms persist you should seek a medical diagnosis.

Tension headaches are often caused by a contraction of the muscles that cover the skull, especially at the base of the skull where the trapezius neck muscles meet the head, and around the jaw. A tension headache often feels like an unpleasant tightness around the head, and pressure over the eyebrows. The pain is distracting but should still allow you to function, and will not be accompanied by the nausea or light or sound sensitivity associated with migraines.

How it works

The rubbing action on the forehead may send signals to the brain to relax the muscles at back of the neck, easing the pain. Also, the sharp fragrance encourages a relaxation of the jaw and an opening of the sinuses, which can also release the build-up of tension. After applying the lime remedy you can further ease trapezius muscle stiffness by rolling your shoulders back several times so that your shoulder blades feel like they are being pinched together and then follow this by gently turning your head from side to side to look over each shoulder.

>Verdict

There is no scientific proof that limes can cure a headache but the anecdotal evidence is strong.

" It is not good for a child to be born with any teeth showing "

/ Natal teeth have been reported since Roman times and have been viewed by different cultures as either a blessing or a curse. Several historical figures were born with a few teeth already showing, such as Napoleon , Richard III, Louis XIV and Hannibal. In some parts of Europe it was believed that babies born with teeth were destined to become great soldiers, while in China, India and Africa natal teeth were considered monstrous or demonic and babies were exorcised or killed to destroy the evil spirits within them.

Even today the myth persists that these teeth are in some way unpleasant, either because "the sooner they come in the sooner they fall out" or because some people view them as precocious or symptomatic of a medical defect or condition.

Scarce but safe
The good news is that while natal teeth are relatively uncommon, they pose no risk to the baby (apart from causing little ulcers on the tongue in some cases), and while they might make breastfeeding painful for the mother, the baby is spared some of the pain of teething six months later.

The incidence of natal teeth ranges from 1:2,000 to 1:3,500 live births and the condition is slightly more common in females. The majority of natal teeth are the premature eruption of normal teeth (rather than extra teeth), they usually occur in pairs (the eruption of more than two natal teeth is rare – more than 1 in 30,000 live births) and in more than 85 per cent of cases they are the lower primary central incisors. Natal teeth can either look normal or be smaller, conical and yellowish with poor root formation.

Causes

The exact cause of natal teeth is still unknown, but as Alexander Leung from the University of Calgary, Canada detailed in an article in the *Journal of the National Medical Association* in 2006, "infection, febrile states, trauma, malnutrition, superficial position of the tooth germ, hormonal stimulation and maternal exposure to environmental toxins have been implicated as causative factors".

Treatment

No treatment is necessary unless they are very loose or if they are extra teeth hindering the development of normal teeth.

>Verdict

In the vast majority of cases natal teeth pose no risk to the baby, are not indicative of another underlying problem and have very little impact on future development or life chances.

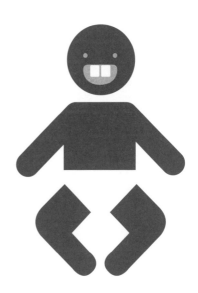

" A newborn licked by a dog will be a quick healer "

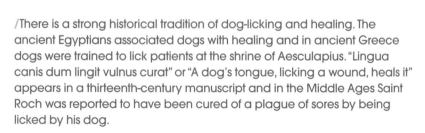

/There is a strong historical tradition of dog-licking and healing. The ancient Egyptians associated dogs with healing and in ancient Greece dogs were trained to lick patients at the shrine of Aesculapius. "Lingua canis dum lingit vulnus curat" or "A dog's tongue, licking a wound, heals it" appears in a thirteenth-century manuscript and in the Middle Ages Saint Roch was reported to have been cured of a plague of sores by being licked by his dog.

Dog saliva

Dog saliva has also been the subject of much misinformation. According to a recent study by a leading manufacturer of pet dental chews and treats, two common beliefs among pet owners are that a dog's mouth is cleaner than a human's and that a pet's saliva can disinfect human cuts and scrapes. For many years medical literature supported the belief that a bite from a human was more likely to become infected than a dog bite. In fact none of these are the case.

Misleading medical literature

Medical literature has helped to seed this misinformation because when it showed that human bites are more likely to become infected than those of other mammals, folk wisdom spread that dog bites were safer than human bites. Unfortunately these earlier studies didn't compare like with like since the high levels of infection were skewed by a high proportion of injuries that weren't really bites at all, but the result of closed-fist injuries (sustained from punching someone in the mouth) presenting to doctors after infection was already established.

Statistically, human bites on other areas of the body pose the same risk of infection as animal bites. According to a 1995 review in the *Journal of the American Academy of Dermatology:* "Human bite wounds have long had a bad reputation for severe infection and frequent complication. However, recent data demonstrate that human bites occurring anywhere other than the hand present no more of a risk for infection than any other type of mammalian bite."

Plaque and tartar

Dogs' mouths are not cleaner than human mouths; they are riddled with germs and bacteria, just like our own, but dogs commonly have a greater build-up of germ-harbouring plaque and tartar on their teeth than humans.

Histatins and nerve growth factor

Wound-licking is an instinctive behaviour in many animals. The licking action can clean dirt and debris from a wound and saliva contains simple proteins called histatins which fight infections and encourage the skin to grow over a wound more quickly. Researchers at the University of Florida at Gainesville have discovered a protein called Nerve Growth Factor (NGF) in saliva and research by Dr Nigel Benjamin at St Bartholomew's Hospital and the London School of Medicine and Dentistry has shown that the nitrite in saliva forms nitric oxide on the skin, which helps to protect against bacterial infections.

A little dirt is good for you
There is strong evidence that saliva has healing properties and that exposing children to dirt, and even the intestinal worms commonly found in domestic pets such as cats and dogs, can strengthen their immune systems.

Medically this is known as the "Hygiene Hypothesis". Mary Ruebush, a microbiology and immunology instructor and author of *Why Dirt Is Good* explains: "What a child is doing when he puts things in his mouth is allowing his immune response to explore his environment. Not only does this allow for 'practice' of immune responses, which will be necessary for protection, but it also plays a critical role in teaching the immature immune response what is best ignored."

Intestinal worms
Studies by Dr Joel Weinstock from Tufts Medical Centre in Boston and Dr David Elliott at the University of Iowa suggest that intestinal worms are "likely to be the biggest player" in programming the infant immune response even more effectively than bacterial and viral infections. Elliott advises: "Children should be allowed to go barefoot in the dirt, play in the dirt, and not have to wash their hands when they come in to eat … (and) have two dogs and a cat," which will expose them to intestinal worms, boost their immune system and make them less likely to develop allergies and autoimmune diseases.

>Verdict

There is no scientific evidence proving that newborns who are licked by a dog become quicker healers, because no one has bothered to test this superstition, but the Hygiene Hypothesis and recent research indicates that the infant immune response benefits from exposure to microorganisms and animals.

"Cure leg cramps by sleeping with a bar of soap"

SOAP

/The popular American syndicated talk show *The Doctors* recently covered this topic. Co-host Dr Jim Sears introduced the subject: "Well I actually had never heard about this so I looked at the literature and I couldn't find any studies that showed that this works but apparently a lot of you guys out there swear by it."

This remedy appears time and time again in blogs and home remedy websites. *The Doctors* ran a twitter poll to see how many viewers were familiar with this technique and 42 per cent said that putting a bar of soap in their bed had helped their feet or leg cramps. However, host Dr Travis Stork quickly dismissed it, saying, "But again, probably no scientific basis for that" and moved on to the next question without any attempt to analyse the claims further.

Anecdotal evidence

This indicates that the size of the bar doesn't matter, since people have reported success with large bars and small hotel bars, wrapped and unwrapped. Some people place the soap underneath the fitted sheet, others keep it in an old stocking; many report the greatest relief when their feet are actually touching the soap. It has also been commonly reported that the effect stops working when the soap is a few months old, so using a fresh bar of soap appears to be significant.

However, the fact remains that there are no peer-reviewed double-blind scientific studies of this phenomenon, so scientifically all we can say is that there is currently no evidence. However, it is hard to ignore the thousands of people who say it has cured their cramps, or anecdotal evidence by people who have secretly used a bar of soap on their partners and had positive results, supposedly ruling out the placebo effect. So what chemical processes could be taking place?

There are many possible benefits

The first is the placebo effect: cramp sufferers report improvements simply because they believe the remedy works. Since one of the causes of cramps is muscle tension, feeling calmer and more relaxed would have an impact.

The scent of the soap may help to distract a cramp sufferer from the pain, causing them to relax their leg, easing the cramps. Many studies, such as the research at James Cook University in Australia, has shown that smells, especially sweet smells, seem to help people tolerate pain because they target the emotion centres of the brain.

Chemically, soap is a salt of a fatty acid. It is made by mixing vegetable or animal oils and fats with a strongly alkaline solution to produce sodium stearate or potassium stearate. Nanoscopic metals are commonly added to modern soaps for colour and their anti-bacterial properties: these commonly include titanium powder, nickel and aluminium. Since this remedy is long established, these modern additives are probably insignificant, so one of the active ingredients may be sodium or potassium. Many leg cramps are associated with dehydration and depletion of calcium, potassium or magnesium but it is unclear why soap in the bed is any more effective at delivering potassium ions than showering with soap. Cramps can

also be caused by a build-up of lactic acid; soap is an alkali, but again it is hard to see how the acid and alkali could interact through the skin.

Hand-made soaps usually contain glycerine (commercial soap manufacturers remove this by-product of the soap-making process for use in hydrating beauty creams). Glycerine is a humectant – it attracts moisture to the skin, but it cannot hydrate cramping legs; drinking a glass of water should be more effective.

> Verdict

There is no scientific explanation for this technique, but many people claim to gain relief. Soap in the bed isn't harmful, so if you suffer from leg cramps it is definitely worth a try, since science hasn't disproved its effectiveness yet either.

SOAP

Sodium Stearate – a major component of soap:

$$C_{18}H_{36}O_2Na$$

" Putting butter on a burn eases the pain "

/Take a look inside your first-aid kit and you'll see dressings, elastic bandages, antiseptic wipes, painkillers and a conspicuous absence of butter, lard or any other oil-based substance commonly found in the kitchen – and with good reason. You should never put butter on a burn.

Close to hand

It is easy to see how this remedy became popular. People frequently get burned in kitchens and butter is close to hand. Butter is oily and natural, it coats the burn and maybe even cools it down if it has been kept in a cool place, such as a refrigerator or pantry, and prevents infection. In fact the opposite is true: butter can cause an infection, slows the release of heat from the burn and creates an environment for bacterial growth.

Treatment

The best treatment for a burn is to immediately run the affected area under cold water for several minutes to cool it down and clean it.

Act quickly. The quicker you can start cooling down the injury the less damage will be done. Many people make the mistake of cooling a burn for too short a time. Even a minor burn can require fifteen minutes of cooling. Don't use ice or ice-cold water as this can damage the skin – extreme cold can damage and destroy skin cells as effectively as extreme heat.

Remove clothing that is covering the burn as it can retain heat, but do not try to remove clothing that has stuck to the skin.

Then cover the burn with a sterile gauze or non-adhesive bandage to prevent infection. Avoid fluffy materials like cotton wool as these will stick to the wound. If blisters form, don't pop them – this only increases the risk of infection.

Clingfilm

You may have heard of clingfilm being used to cover a burn. If sterile gauze is unavailable, clingfilm is suitable, so long as you discard the first few inches (which may contain germs), use a single layer and don't wrap too tightly because this will cause pressure and discomfort if swelling occurs. When the emergency services arrive they will be able to see the skin damage through the transparent clingfilm and remove it easily when required.

>Verdict

Butter spread on a burn does not ease the pain, it increases it, because it helps to trap the heat within the skin. It also increases the risk of infection.

"You can get the flu from the flu vaccine"

/There are three different flu shots (each contains three seasonal influenza viruses) plus a nasal-spray flu vaccine; the shots use dead viruses and the nasal spray uses a weakened flu virus. None of the flu vaccines can actually cause the flu.

Influenza disease trends

There are 130 national influenza centres in 101 countries which continually monitor influenza and study influenza disease trends worldwide. A flu shot contains three seasonal influenza viruses that are cultured in eggs. The choice of viruses can change each year,

depending on which strains the national influenza centres predict will be the most prevalent in the forthcoming season. For example, the 2011–2012 flu vaccine in the Northern Hemisphere protected against an influenza A (H1N1) virus, an influenza A (H3N2) virus and an influenza B virus.

Regular seasonal flu shot

The regular seasonal flu shot is "intramuscular" (injected into muscle) and is approved for use in people six months of age and older, including people with chronic medical conditions and pregnant women. A high-dose intramuscular vaccine is available for people 65 and older and contains four times the amount of antigen (the part of the vaccine that encourages the immune system to make antibodies). Thirdly, an intradermal vaccine (injected into skin) is available for people 18 to 64 years of age.

Complications

Certain groups of people are at risk of complications and should consult with a doctor before getting a flu shot, but this does not mean that they will develop the flu. These include people who have had a severe allergic reaction to eggs or a previous flu shot, people who have a fever, pregnant women and anyone who has had Guillain-Barré Syndrome (a severe paralytic illness affecting the peripheral nervous system).

Antibodies

The effectiveness of the vaccine depends on the age and immune system of the subject, plus the strains of flu to which they are exposed. It takes about two weeks for your body to develop antibodies after vaccination, so if you develop flu during this time it means that either you were exposed to the virus before vaccination or before your body was able to develop antibodies. Alternatively, you may have been exposed to a strain of flu that wasn't present in the vaccine.

Side-effects

However, the vaccine is not without its side-effects (still not the flu), which include soreness, redness, itching or swelling where the needle went in, mild fever and aches. These usually only last for one or two days. The most common symptom, soreness, is caused by the immune system making protective antibodies. The possible side-effects of the nasal spray include a runny nose, headache, sore throat and cough in adults, and runny nose, headache, wheezing, vomiting, muscle aches and fever in children.

>Verdict

It is still possible to catch the flu after getting vaccinated, but you cannot develop the flu as a result of the vaccine.

" Long hot baths reduce sperm count "

/The negative effect of heat on male fertility has been known since ancient times and appears in Hippocratic texts from the fifth century BC. Although the advice that hot baths reduce sperm count has been in circulation for centuries, there have only been a handful of recently published studies, but they do support the theory.

Temporary sterilisation

In 1946 Swiss doctor M. Voegeli spent ten years experimenting with hot water as an inexpensive and universally available form of male contraception, especially for developing countries (she practised in India). She used nine volunteers and achieved temporary sterilisation (lasting for six months) by having her subjects sit in a shallow or testes-only bath of 116°F for forty-five minutes daily for three weeks. Water at lower temperatures resulted in shorter periods of infertility (water at 110° produced at least four months of infertility).

Wet heat

The next major study linking hot baths with fertility took place in 1965. Men were exposed to "wet heat" for 30 minutes every other day and observed a temporary decrease in sperm production, but the study did not measure sperm quality before and afterwards.

Improved fertility

In 2007 a three-year study of eleven men with fertility problems reported that six of the men experienced a five-fold increase in sperm production after avoiding hot baths for six months. Sperm motility also increased nearly three-fold, from 12 per cent to 34 per cent. The other five men showed no improvement but the researchers suspect that this might have been due to them being heavy smokers. Three of the men who increased their fertility were occasional smokers.

It's cold outside

Testes need to stay cooler than the rest of the body in order to produce healthy sperm, which is why the testes are kept in a sack outside the abdomen. Sperm production stops when the temperature of the testicles is raised to 98 degrees. The skin of the scrotum tightens in response to the cold – the tighter the skin the closer it pulls the testes to the rest of the body to raise their temperature. Also, a heat exchange occurs between incoming and outgoing blood vessels, like in the coils of a refrigerator, to regulate the temperature.

Sperm count is also seasonal – the lowest count is during the summer, when the weather is warmest. The quality and motility of the sperm is more affected by heat than is the quantity. Some sources say that sperm counts return to normal levels within a few days to a week of having a hot bath, while others, like the Voegeli study, indicate that sperm is affected for several months.

>Verdict

Hot baths do reduce sperm count and motility, but scientists disagree on how long these effects last. You are advised against using hot baths as a stand-alone method of contraception, but if you are having problems conceiving, take a warm shower instead and quit smoking.

"Sitting on a hot radiator or cold wall causes piles"

/Piles, also known as haemorrhoids, are swollen and inflamed blood vessels in the anal canal which can be itchy and/or painful. They have several causes but sitting on a hot radiator or a cold wall is not one of them.

The anal canal is a short, muscular tube that connects your rectum (final straight portion of the large intestine) with your anus (the external opening that is controlled by sphincter muscles). Piles are round swellings in the anal canal that develop most commonly from straining during a bowel movement.

Pile grades

Although piles develop in the anal canal they are graded in increasing degrees of severity and can often hang outside the anus: first degree piles may bleed but can't be seen outside the anus; second degree piles protrude during a bowel movement but go back inside the anal canal afterwards; third degree piles hang outside but can be pushed back in; fourth degree piles hang down but can't be pushed back inside.

Risk factors

Piles can happen to anyone (fifty per cent of people have had them at some time in their life) but they are more common in people over 65 and those who are overweight. Other risk factors include a diet low in fibre, pregnancy, lifting heavy objects or a congenital weakness in the rectum.

Treatment and prevention

Increasing fibre intake, staying well hydrated, getting plenty of exercise and taking warm baths will reduce the need to strain on the toilet and often reduces piles naturally. Piles often get better by themselves after a few days but anti-inflammatory creams and suppositories can reduce the swelling.

If further treatment is required, a band is placed above the pile to cut off the blood supply and make the pile shrink. The pile can be injected with an oily solution (sclerotherapy) or laser treatment can cauterise the vein or it can be burned off with electrotherapy. Surgery to remove the piles may be required for severe cases if none of these solutions work.

>Verdict

Sitting on a hot radiator may cause existing piles to swell and become more uncomfortable, but it doesn't cause them. Sitting on a cold wall may actually bring some relief but sitting down for long periods often makes piles worse, regardless of the temperature of the surface.

" Add a penny to a vase to make tulips stand up straight "

/ Just one of the many uses of a shiny new copper penny is to make tulips stand to attention, if centuries of folklore are to be believed. Today science has several chemistry-based reasons to support the practice, but many horticultural experts advise that a clean vase and water are the best combination to keep tulips from falling over.

Twenty years ago before copper prices soared, many low-denomination coins were more than ninety per cent copper. Today many countries including the UK and US have switched to the cheaper option of copper-coated steel or zinc, so the copper content has dropped to just a few per cent. Despite this, the three main scientific reasons why copper coins may help tulips to stand tall should remain unaffected. They are:

1/ Plants need seventeen elements for growth: carbon, hydrogen and oxygen (found in air or water), six macronutrients (nitrogen, potassium, magnesium, calcium, sulphur and phosphorous) and eight micronutrients which are found in the soil: copper, iron, zinc, cobalt, chlorine, boron, molybdenum and manganese. These micronutrients are absorbed through the roots in a soil-water solution. Putting copper in the water allows some copper ions to be absorbed through the cut stem, prolonging the integrity and strength of the cell walls.

2/ Copper acts as a fungicide. The vase should have been cleaned with hot soapy water to eliminate bacteria and fungi, which are a major cause of damage to cut flowers. Under certain conditions concentrations of positive ions of some metals including silver, gold, brass and copper do have antibacterial properties known as the "oligodynamic effect" (see page 36).

3/ Copper slightly increases the acidity (decreases the pH) of the water.

Shortened lifespan

Despite all this, Dutch flower bulb expert, Frans Roozen, technical director of the International Flower Bulb Centre in Hillegom, Holland, says, "Tulips are self-sufficient. Just add clean water, that's all." People who add copper to the vase, "see immediate results with their own eyes and say 'yes it is true!' But what they see is merely a mini-surge of energy in the flower and not the aftermath, which is often a shortened lifespan."

Cutting technique

Cut the stems diagonally using a sharp un-serrated knife. This creates a wider surface area through which the stem can absorb water; it also prevents the cut end from becoming jammed at the bottom of the vase, cutting off water supply. Cut tulips in the morning when their water and stored food content is highest. Plants grown from bulbs (like tulips) prefer cool water. Keep the vase away from direct heat and sunlight.

Piercing the stem

Many florists use another method to keep their tulips straight. The cut flowers continue to grow, which makes them droop, but this growth can be halted by piercing through the stem with a sharp knife just below the base of the flower.

Finally, many florists swear by a method that is time-consuming but 100 per cent reliable – they wire all the stems before putting them in an arrangement.

>Verdict

Copper may create a short-term improvement but actually damage the lifespan of the cut flower. Using a clean vase and clean water with a little commercial plant food, plus re-cutting the stem ends every few days, will show better results than a single copper penny.

"Heartburn during pregnancy means a hairy baby "

/Over half of pregnant women are affected by heartburn. It is one of the most common pregnancy-related conditions and is normally not a cause for alarm. Heartburn occurs when acid from the stomach passes up through the oesophagus and causes a burning sensation and sour acidic taste in the throat and back of the mouth. It can feel as if food is stuck in the throat and can be accompanied by chest pain or tightness. For years doctors have dismissed a link between heartburn and the hairiness of the newborn but recent research, albeit with a small sample, has proved that there is indeed a strong correlation.

Hormonal changes
Later in the pregnancy the baby is large enough to push up on the stomach and cause the acid reflux that leads to heartburn. Normally the sphincter muscle at the base of the oesophagus is strong enough to prevent digestive juices from leaving the stomach, but during pregnancy hormonal changes relax the smooth muscles of the uterus, allowing it to expand, and they also relax this sphincter.

Strong correlation
A recent study by scientists at Johns Hopkins University has found a strong correlation between heartburn and the hairiness of the newborn and attributes the

hormones responsible for relaxing the sphincter for also influencing the hair growth. The results of the study were first published in the journal *Birth* in December 2006.

Sixty-four pregnant women were studied, 78 per cent of them reported some heartburn and they were asked to rank its severity. Shortly after birth two photographs were taken of the babies' heads; these photos were assessed by independent observers who rated the degree of hairiness of each baby. The study abstract points out that "Symptom severity was unrelated to foetal sex and maternal characteristics including parity, age or weight. The simple linear relationship between heartburn severity and hair volume was significant." Twenty-eight of the women reported severe heartburn and 23 of them (82 per cent) had babies with average or above-average hairiness. Ten out of the twelve women who reported no heartburn (83 per cent) had babies with little or no hair.

The lead author, Kathleen Costigan, a registered nurse in the Department of Gynecology and Obstetrics at Johns Hopkins, was surprised at these results: "Contrary to expectations, it appears that an association between heartburn severity during pregnancy and newborn hair does exist. We've heard this claim hundreds of times, and I've always told people it's nonsense. Since the study came out, I've had to eat a lot of crow."

She has speculated that the reason for the link is that higher levels of the hormones oestrogen and progesterone relax the oesophageal sphincter, leading to increased heartburn. Progesterone also slows down the wavelike contractions of the intestines, slowing digestion. Other studies have shown that these same hormones increase hair growth in the developing baby.

> Verdict

Despite the small sample size there does appear to be a linear link between hairiness and heartburn: the greater the heartburn the greater the likelihood of a hairy baby.

" Eating your greens makes your hair curl "

/ For years parents told their children that their hair would curl if they ate their greens but this is only partially true. The quality and health of hair is definitely related to the quality of the food we eat, since proper nutrition and ample hydration is essential for strong, healthy, shiny hair. Hair curliness is genetic, but certain green vegetables contain sulphur, which is an important component in hair structure, so while eating your greens may cause curly hair to become curlier, it won't turn straight hair curly.

Dominant characteristic

The structure of curly hair is different from that of straight hair; it is determined by the shape of the follicle, which is genetic.

If one of your parents had curly hair there is a good chance you will too because curliness is a dominant characteristic. The direction of hair growth determines whether hair is curly or straight. If the follicle points towards the surface of the skin and the hair shaft has a round cross-section, the hair is straight; if the follicle is curved and the hair shaft has an oval cross-section, the hair is curly.

Keratin and disulphide bonds

Hair, like your nails, is primarily made of a protein called keratin, which is made of protein with sulphur atoms bonded together in disulphide bonds. The amount of curliness is also determined by the number of disulphide bonds between the hair proteins, so if you have curly hair, eating sulphur-rich greens may make it curlier but will not make straight hair curly.

Greens aid blood flow

You need to eat your greens for healthy, strong, shiny hair. Green vegetables are also high in iron, which is an important part of delivering oxygen in the blood throughout the body, including the scalp. Good blood flow to the scalp means healthy hair; poor blood flow can lead to hair loss. Greens like spinach are a good source of Vitamin A which is important for hair flexibility and prevents it from becoming brittle. Green leafy vegetables also provide silica, which is important for hair strength.

Sulphur and protein

Sulphur is also vital for hair condition; it is connected with the amino acids cysteine and methionine. Hair thickness and richness depends on sulphur and other vitamins and minerals, so eat your greens for healthy hair. Other foods that are rich in sulphur include radish, cabbage, Brussels sprouts, broccoli and onion.

Since hair is made of protein, you need good quality protein to make your hair healthy. Lack of protein leads to limp, thin, dull hair. Make sure you are getting your recommended daily allowance of high quality protein from soy, nuts, dairy, lean meats, fish and eggs, and especially walnuts, salmon and flax seeds, which are also high in omega-3 fatty acids.

>Verdict

Eating your greens helps to maintain healthy hair, but cannot make straight hair curly.

❝Hot water slakes thirst better than cold❞

/The American College of Sports Medicine recommends that for exercise, chilled water and drinks should be used because cold water also reduces your body temperature, thus reducing further water loss through excessive sweating.

If you are exercising for more than one hour you should rehydrate using sports drinks to replace carbohydrate and electrolytes. If you are in very cold conditions, you need to preserve body heat so you should be drinking hot drinks for rehydration otherwise your body will waste energy heating a cold fluid. However, regardless of temperature, warm water actually hydrates the body more quickly than cold because it passes through the stomach and into the bloodstream more quickly.

Vasopressin and plasma osmolality
An important factor in the maintenance of fluid balance is the secretion of anti-diuretic hormone (ADH), also known as vasopressin, which makes you feel thirsty. It is secreted by the hypothalamus when plasma osmolality (concentration of dissolved substances in the blood) increases due to dehydration. Cold water activates receptors in your throat which inhibit the secretion of vasopressin so you feel quenched. This is why pregnant women are given ice chips during

labour so that they can slake their thirst without drinking lots of fluids, which could cause problems if emergency surgery becomes necessary.

Edward Deaux's Paradox

An article in *New Scientist*, October 11, 1973 entitled "Warm drinks don't quench thirst; but they do really" examined the apparent paradox of a thirst experiment by Edward Deaux of the department of psychology, Antioch College, Ohio. Deaux gave thirsty rats water at 12°C, 24°C and 37°C and found that they drank significantly less of the cold water, suggesting that cold water was more thirst-quenching than warm. At first he thought the rats might be drinking less cold water to avoid hyperthermia, so he reduced their body temperature artificially and found that the consumption of both warm and cool water reduced equally, proving that body temperature was not a relevant factor.

Then he looked at plasma osmolality. Studies have shown that the time between drinking and eating depends on the speed and degree of plasma osmolality. Deaux found that the rats began eating sooner after drinking warm water than cold, suggesting that the warm water reached the bloodstream and hydrated the body more quickly than cold. This didn't make sense because the rats drank less of the cold water, suggesting that they felt hydrated more quickly. Deaux explained the apparent paradox by stomach distention, since cold water passes more slowly through the stomach: "The paradox suggests that temperature-dependent gastric factors and water-transport factors determine stomach distention cues of thirst satiation."

Hydration v. thirst quenching

So warm water does hydrate more quickly than cold, but cold water is more thirst-quenching. Stomach distention is greater with cold water, because it stays in the stomach longer, reducing the feeling of thirst. However, as Alexandra W. Logue points out in her book *The Psychology of Eating and Drinking*, "if you're one of the people who thinks that a cold drink is the best way to quench your thirst, that's only true for a very short period of time after you drink. Over the long term, the best way to quench your thirst is to drink more water."

>Verdict

Cold water quenches but warm water actually hydrates more quickly.

"Red sky at night, shepherd's delight. Red sky in morning, shepherd's warning"

/Most people in both the northern and southern hemispheres are familiar with this particular bit of weather lore, and with good reason: it's true. A red sunset usually presages dry weather the following day and a red sunrise usually heralds bad weather on the way during that day. This saying has been around for hundreds of years and even appears in the Bible.

In Matthew 16:2-3 when some Pharisees and Sadducees ask Jesus to show them a sign from heaven, "He answered and said unto them, When it is evening, ye say, It will be fair weather: for the sky is red. And in the morning, It will be foul weather to day: for the sky is red and lowering. O ye hypocrites, ye can discern the face of the sky; but can ye not discern the signs of the times?"

William Shakespeare makes reference to the adage in his 1593 poem Venus and Adonis:

"Like a red morn that ever yet betokened,

Wreck to the seaman, tempest to the field,

Sorrow to the shepherds, woe unto the birds,

Gusts and foul flaws to herdmen and to herds."

Storm systems usually move from west to east, blown by westerly winds. The sun rises in the east and sets in the west. When the sun is setting, if there are moisture-bearing clouds travelling away from the viewer and moving to the east, the sun's light will illuminate their undersides, and show up as a red light because it passes through the thickest part of the atmosphere at a low angle and most of the shorter wavelengths of lights – the blues and greens – are scattered. In the morning the opposite happens to create a red sky – sunlight from the east illuminates clouds in the west, which will move eastward during the day and bring bad weather to the viewer (unless the rain clouds rain themselves dry before they arrive).

>Verdict

Deep red sunsets often precede dry, settled weather; a red sky in the morning is often associated with a stormy weather front travelling from the west.

"Chew more, eat less "

/In the nineteenth century an American health food guru called Horace Fletcher became rich and famous through a technique which he named "Fletcherizing". He encouraged his followers to chew their food thirty-two times – one for each tooth or 100 times a minute – before swallowing it.

Nicknamed "The Great Masticator", Fletcher peddled the mantra "Nature will castigate those who don't masticate" but by the time of his death in 1919 the world had moved on to calorie counting. However, a recent study by nutritionists in China has found that young men who chewed each mouthful forty times instead of fifteen, consumed 12 per cent fewer calories.

Jie Li and his colleagues from the School of Public Health at Harbin Medical University studied thirty young men, 16 lean and 14 obese, and published their results in the *American Journal of Clinical Nutrition*. They found that the obese individuals ate more quickly and chewed fewer times than their lean counterparts, despite having a similar bite size. Then they offered the same test meal to both groups on two separate occasions. During the first meal participants were instructed to chew each mouthful fifteen times; during the second meal they were instructed to chew each mouthful forty times. Both groups consumed 11.9 per cent fewer calories during the second meal.

Ghrelin and cholecystokinin
Chewing more also affected levels of two important hormones in the bloodstream, which were measured after each meal. Chewing each mouthful forty times resulted in lower blood levels of ghrelin, a chemical that stimulates appetite, and higher levels of cholecystokinin, also known as CCK, a gastrointestinal hormone which triggers the release of digestive enzymes and bile from the pancreas and gallbladder and also acts as a hunger suppressant.

These results are promising for possible future treatment of obesity but the effects may differ with other groups. For example, increasing CCK levels in rats significantly reduces hunger in young males, but is slightly less effective in older animals, and even less effective in females.

We don't chew everything

If an average person reduced their calorie intake by 12 per cent they would lose nearly 25 pounds in a year, but we don't chew everything that passes our lips – ice cream, drinks and soup can still pile on the pounds.

However, many nutritionists aim to help their clients to eat more mindfully rather than just shovel food in without thinking. Chewing longer should make people more aware of how and what they are eating, and allows more time for the hormones which signal satiety to the brain to take effect.

Drink your food

A Taoist recommendation for healthy eating is, "Drink your food" – chew it so thoroughly that it liquefies. This allows digestive enzymes in the saliva to break down the food even more before it reaches the stomach so that more nutrients can be extracted. But if someone with an obsessive relationship with food followed this advice they might conceivably end up eating the same amount but gain weight, because their digestive system had managed to extract more calories from the food.

Earlier studies have found no link between chewing and calories consumed and many scientists, including Adam Drewnowski, director of the University of Washington Center for Obesity Research in Seattle are sceptical: "I suppose that if you chew each bite of food 100 times or more you may end up eating less. However, I am not sure that this is a viable obesity prevention measure."

>Verdict

If an average person reduced their calorie intake by 12 per cent they would lose nearly 25 pounds in a year, but we don't chew everything that passes our lips – ice cream, drinks and soup can still pile on the pounds.

"Shine windows with vinegar and scrunched-up newspaper"

/Scrunched-up newspaper and vinegar have been used to clean windows for several generations; they are supposed to leave a smear-free finish and some say a great shine too. However, the ink composition of newspapers has changed during the last thirty years, so this may not be as effective a remedy as it was half a century ago.

Ink composition

Some critics claim that new soy-based inks leave streaks, while the old petroleum-based inks didn't. However, soy ink is blended with similar pigments, resins and waxes as the oil inks were (to help the ink dry more quickly and prevent the ink from rubbing off), so it should still make for a good shine. An advantage of soy ink is that it allows a reduction in coverage, so there's less ink on the paper to dirty your hands.

112

For regular cleaning

Mix three parts water with one part white vinegar. Soak an old cotton towel in the cleaning solution and rub on the window, then dry and polish to a shine using scrunched-up newspaper.

Why it works

The newspaper soaks up the moisture, but it also has a fine abrasive action, as the minute particles of ink and resin polish the surface, lubricated by the ink oils. The vinegar in the water is an acid, and breaks down grease, bacteria, mould and water mineral deposits. The newspaper ink does not come off on the window but it will smudge onto the window frames, so make sure you only rub the window with the newspaper. The ink doesn't rub off on the glass because it is shiny and non porous. It is easier for the dirt to be picked up by the newspaper. The glass repels water while the newspaper absorbs it – a perfect match.

Other benefits

Newspapers are lint free so they are more effective than paper towels, which always leave fine particles of paper on the glass, or many fabrics which shed fibres. High-quality paper contains solids such as calcium carbonate and silica, which can scratch the glass. Older newspapers used oil-based inks which some critics say will smear the glass more than modern newspapers which use water- /soy-based inks.

>Verdict

Despite advances in ink technology, newspaper and vinegar is still an effective method of cleaning windows and leaving them dry and smear free.

"An apple a day keeps the doctor away "

/In 2004 Jeanelle Boyer and Rui H. Liu from the Department of Food Science and Institute of Comparative and Environmental Toxicology, Cornell University published the article, "Apple phytochemicals and their health benefits". The purpose of the paper was to pull together all the recent literature about the health benefits of apples, "their phytochemical profile, bioavailability of apple phytochemicals, and factors that may affect the phytochemical quality, such as apple variety, ripening, storage, and processing".

The electronic version of the article is the complete one and can be found online at: http://www.nutritionj.com/content/3/1/5. It gives apples a glowing reference and after reading it you'd be unusual if you weren't inspired to add an apple to your daily diet. Below are some excerpted sections of the Open Access article:

Cancer

Several studies have specifically linked apple consumption with a reduced risk for cancer, especially lung cancer. In the Nurses' Health Study and the Health Professionals' Follow-up Study, involving over 77,000 women and 47,000 men, women who consumed at least one serving per day of apples and pears had a reduced risk of lung cancer. Of the men involved, there was no association seen between any individual fruit or vegetable and lung cancer risk.

Cardiovascular disease

A reduced risk of cardiovascular disease has been associated with apple consumption. The Women's Health Study surveyed nearly 40,000 women with a 6.9-year follow-up, and examined the association between flavonoids and cardiovascular disease. Women ingesting the highest amounts of flavonoids had a 35% reduction in risk of cardiovascular events.

Asthma and pulmonary function

Apple consumption has been inversely linked with asthma and has also been positively associated with general pulmonary health. In a recent study involving 1600 adults in Australia, apple and pear intake was associated with a decreased risk of asthma and a decrease in bronchial hypersensitivity, but total fruit and vegetable intake was not associated with asthma risk or severity.

Diabetes and weight loss

Not only may apples help decrease the risk of heart disease, cancer and asthma, but apple consumption may also be associated with a lower risk for diabetes. In a Finnish study of 10,000 people, a reduced risk of Type II diabetes was associated with apple consumption.

Antioxidant activity

Apples, and especially apple peel, have been found to have a potent antioxidant activity and can greatly inhibit the growth of liver cancer and colon cancer cells.

Cholesterol-lowering effects

Some of the apple's protective effect against cardiovascular disease may come from its potential cholesterol-lowering ability.

Apple phytochemicals

Apples contain a large concentration of flavonoids as well as a variety of other phytochemicals, and the concentration of these phytochemicals may depend on many factors, such as cultivar of the apple, harvest and storage of the apples, and processing of the apples. The concentration of phytochemicals also varies greatly between the apple peel and the apple flesh.

Because the apple peel contains more antioxidant compounds, especially quercetin, apple peel may have higher antioxidant activity and higher bioactivity than the apple flesh. Research showed that apples without the peel had less antioxidant activity than apples with the peel.

Some of the most well studied antioxidant compounds in apples include quercetin-3-galactoside, quercetin-3-glucoside, quercetin-3-rhamnoside, catechin, epicatechin, procyanidin, cyanidin-3-galactoside, coumaric acid, chlorogenic acid, gallic acid, and phloridzin.

>Verdict

In numerous epidemiological studies, apples have been associated with a decreased risk of chronic diseases such as cardiovascular disease, cancer and asthma.

In vitro and animal studies have demonstrated that apples have high antioxidant activity, can inhibit cancer cell proliferation, decrease lipid oxidation, and lower cholesterol, potentially explaining their role in reducing risk of chronic disease.

Apples contain a wide variety of phytochemicals, many of which have been found to have strong antioxidant activity and anticancer activity.

"Drinking warm milk makes you sleepy"

/There are several possible reasons why drinking a soothing cup of warm milk helps some people to sleep, but on closer inspection none of them are scientifically proven and the effect may be nothing more than a placebo:

1/ Studies show that animals go to sleep more easily when they are comfortably warm, but if a slight increase in body temperature was the reason for milk-induced drowsiness, any warm nightcap would have the same effect, so there must be another factor.

2/ It is possible that adults who drink warm milk create a pleasant unconscious association with a happy secure postprandial baby state, but no research has examined this phenomenon in adults, although a study published in a recent issue of *Neuroendrocrinology Letters* found that babies go to sleep faster after feedings.

3/ Milk contains tryptophan, the same amino acid that is found in turkey and is reputed to make people feel sleepy after a large roast turkey dinner. Tryptophan is converted into serotonin, a monoamine neurotransmitter that contributes to feelings of well-being and happiness. However, levels of tryptophan in turkey are the same as in other meats, and unlikely to cause drowsiness. Milk also contains levels of tryptophan that are far too low to make you feel sleepy.

Blood-brain barrier

According to Dr Timothy Morgenthaler, a sleep specialist at the Mayo Clinic, there is no food that can induce sleep in an individual. Furthermore, simply ingesting tryptophan does not mean that it will cross the blood-brain barrier and cause chemical changes in the brain. In fact, a 2003 study by researchers at the Massachusetts Institute of Technology, published in the *American Journal of Clinical Nutrition,* showed that eating protein-rich foods such as milk actually decreased the ability of tryptophan to reach the brain.

Habit and association

The most likely explanation for the soporific effects of warm milk are the positive benefits of habit and association. Night-time rituals are a very important way to establish comfort, predictability, and consistency for children and adults. If drinking warm milk becomes associated with calming preparation for sleep, over time it becomes its own psychological reinforcer, especially if the drinker considers it a soothing rewarding treat – this alone could be enough to stimulate the pleasure centres in the brain and produce a feeling of well-being and relaxation.

>Verdict

If warm milk makes you feel drowsy at bedtime, then you have successfully created a positive association that is a valid part of your night-time routine, but the effects are probably more psychological than physical.

"Buttered toast always lands butter-side down"

/The common breakfast disaster of dropping a piece of toast and watching it land butter-side down is a perfect demonstration of "Murphy's Law" which states that "If something can go wrong, it will."

Anyone familiar with statistics might feel this cannot be the case and that, like the flipping of a coin, they should expect to see a fifty-fifty distribution of head/tale, butter/no butter. This has even been backed up by tests conducted for a BBC TV programme where toast was tossed into the air 300 times and the toast landing showed a 50/50 outcome like a random coin toss. However, as distinguished science journalist Robert Matthews has scientifically proved, "the dynamics of falling toast are indeed rather subtle, and

do depend fairly critically on initial conditions" because in real-life situations toast usually slides off a plate or table and while it is butter-side up.

In 1996 Matthews received an Ig Nobel Prize for his paper "Tumbling toast, Murphy's Law and the fundamental constants" in which he proved that buttered toast is more likely to land butter-side down because of a combination of the laws of physics and the height of human beings and table tops.

Butter bias

First of all he dismissed the importance of the weight of the butter: "The mass of butter added to toast (~4g) is small compared to the mass of the typical slice of toast (~35g), is spread thinly, and passes into the body of the toast. Its contribution to the total moment of inertia of the toast – and thus its effect on the toast's rotational dynamics – is thus negligible."

Insufficient angular rotation

Then he conducted experiments with rectangles of bread and toast, cut from a standard white loaf, that measured 10cm x 7.3cm x 1.5cm and pushed them from a "rigid flat and level platform of kitchen Contiboard, used to model the surface of a clean, uncovered table" to establish the value of the coefficient of static friction between the toast/bread and the lamina and showed that both bread and toast "do not have sufficient angular rotation to land butter-side up following free-fall from a table-top". The bread or toast rotates somewhere between 90 and 270 degrees and because of the height of the table, does not have enough time to come butter-side up again.

Doomed to suffer

The same is true when the bread slides off our plate while we are standing. If the plate was held above our head, the toast would have enough time to rotate further than 270 degrees and thus land butter-side up. But we don't hold plates seven feet in the air, we hold them at waist or chest height, so Matthews concludes: "As humans we're pretty much doomed to suffer the fate of watching toast land butter-side down because we can't be tall enough to give toast enough time to come butter-side up again by the time it hits the floor. We're stuck with it."

Solution

Matthews offers two ways to counter this result: cut your toast into much smaller pieces so the rotation rate is quicker or, as you notice the toast sliding off your plate, pull the plate away sharply and the toast will just descend horizontally to the floor before it has time to break into a spin. Another rather impractical solution would be to build a table or breakfast bar that is seven feet above the ground.

>Verdict

Human evolution and the physical laws which govern the universe mean that toast always has and always will mostly land butter-side down.

"Early to bed and early to rise makes a man healthy, wealthy and wise"

/The over-achieving Founding Father, polymath and early riser Benjamin Franklin lived by his own maxim which first appeared in his *Poor Richard's Almanack* which he published for twenty-six years. He was clearly a morning person who believed that rising early gave him more productive hours in the morning, but since then science has returned mixed results on the effectiveness of this sleep pattern.

Daily calories and junk food

Research from Northwestern University has found that people who stay up late and lie in eat more daily calories than normal sleepers. The sleeping habits of a group of 52 people with an average age of thirty were tracked. The late sleepers went to bed on average at 3:45am and woke at 10:45am while the normal sleepers went to bed by 12:30am and woke by 8:00am. The late sleepers consumed an extra 248 calories each day than normal sleepers, twice as much junk food and half as much fruit and vegetables and had higher body mass indices. Other studies have shown that inadequate sleep is linked to obesity and poor health. But if you are getting seven or eight hours' sleep each night does it really matter when you take them?

Whatever suits you best

Dr Joerg Huber of Roehampton University studied 1,068 adults and found that "There are morning people and evening people, and morning people tend to be healthier and happier as well as having lower body mass indices ... maybe morning types are just better suited to this industrial world we are in than late risers".

Researchers from Southampton University found that late sleepers were no less healthy than normal sleepers although those who spent more than 12 hours a night in bed were one-and-a-half times more likely to die slightly younger: "Our results suggest that, though it may be wise not to spend much more than eight hours in bed each night, the time of going to bed and getting up matters little ... the main message of our study is that you should go to bed when you like and get up when you like."

Bi-modal sleep

Our sleep is influenced as much by culture as it is by nature and one size does not fit all. Recently, even the eight-hour sleep has been called into question. A growing body of evidence indicates that before the seventeenth century and the advent of artificial light, people used to sleep in two four-hour chunks separated by a couple of hours of activity. Waking up during the night may be part of normal human physiology. In the 1990s, psychiatrist Thomas Weir exposed a group of test subjects to fourteen hours of darkness every day for a month and by the end of this period their sleep patterns had become bi-modal – they slept for four hours, woke for one or two hours and then took their second four-hour sleep. The historian Roger Ekirch has written an entire book on the anthropology of nightlife during times past: *At Day's Close: Night in Times Past* details scores of historical references to this sleeping pattern.

Sleep requirements change with age

It is well known that teenagers find it harder to rise early in the morning because their natural sleep pattern favours a late bedtime and late rising, which in the past has been labelled as laziness. Educators are becoming increasingly aware of the need to accommodate this teen sleep pattern to facilitate learning. Many schools now start lessons at 10am or 11am and have seen improvements in learning outcomes. Professor Russell Foster, chairman of Circadian Neuroscience at Brasenose College, Oxford has shown that adolescent brains work better

in the afternoon so it is good for young people to stay in bed for an extra two hours. From the age of twenty the need to lie in gradually subsides until our body clocks reach the pre-teenage level around 55 years of age.

CEOs are very early risers

Wealth and high achievement seem to correspond with early rising in the routines of top CEOs in business, according to a limited study by Jim Citrin at Yahoo! Finance. He sent a survey to 20 CEOs and received 17 replies. Rising early was a shared trait: all of them rose before 6am and almost 80 per cent woke at 5:30am or earlier, and several at 4:30am. This is no surprise. Go-getters with huge responsibility and workload in a business culture where long hours are the norm, forgo sleep to get ahead of the game and to stay ahead of their peers – they rise early because they are driven, they aren't driven because they rise early. However, Simon Cowell famously sleeps in until midday and then works until the early hours of the following morning.

>Verdict

In our busy modern world people who rise early have more time to get things done, but while getting up early has many benefits, the most important factors are how much sleep you need and how much you get, not when you get it.

Healthy

Wealthy

Wise

"Long labour, must be a boy "

/An old midwives' tale holds that a long labour means that the baby is a boy and several recent studies have proved that this is true. Boy babies are more likely to experience complications during birth, although reassuringly the proportion of male and female babies requiring post-natal special care is the same.

Between 1997 and 2000 specialist registrar Dr Maeve Eogan led a study of 8,075 deliveries at the National Maternity Hospital in Dublin, Ireland which was published in the *British Medical Journal*: "To ease anxiety, we often joke to women experiencing problems or prolonged labour that 'it must be a boy' – we wanted to see if there was any truth in this."

The results were statistically significant. Complications arose with 29 per cent of the boy babies against 24 per cent of girl babies. Mothers giving birth to boys had a 50 per cent higher chance of needing a Caesarean section than with girls and a 25 per cent higher chance of requiring forceps. The average length of labour was just over six hours for boys and just under six hours for girls. Boys were more likely to experience distress in the womb and mothers carrying boys were more likely to be given oxytocin, a hormone that stimulates contractions.

One possible reason for the increased complications is that male babies tend to be larger, heavier and have bigger heads than girls, but it does not explain why male babies are more likely to experience distress in the womb. Dr Eogan says this "suggests that there is obviously some sort of inherent vulnerability of male infants to the whole process of labour". It could also be due to differing levels of oestrogen and testosterone in the womb.

Two other recent studies have supported these results: in 2002 a study of 90,000 births found that boys were 50 per cent more likely than girls to suffer an arrest of descent – failure to continue to descend during the second "pushing" stage of labour. A 2009 study of 66,000 deliveries, led by Prof. Marek Glezerman, chairman of the Department of Obstetrics and Gynaecology at the Sackler School of Medicine, Tel Aviv University, found that "pregnancies with a male foetus are more often complicated. They're more likely to result in a premature rupture of the embryonic sac and suffer from premature delivery. And those male foetuses which make it to term, are more likely to suffer from excessive growth in the uterus, making delivery more difficult

and leading to more Caesarean section deliveries."

Prof. Glezerman, an expert in gender-based medicine, doesn't stop there: "...boys are more vulnerable in their life in utero, and this vulnerability continues to exist throughout their lives ... Men are known to have a shorter lifespan, are more susceptible to infections, and have less chance of withstanding disease than women. In short, men are the weaker sex."

>Verdict

Boy babies are slightly more likely to have a longer delivery with complications, but although males are also associated with a slightly higher risk in the neonatal period after birth, boy births should not be classified as high risk or be a cause of anxiety.

127